Topic B1 — Cell Level Systems

Page 2 — Cells and Microscopy

Warm-up

Microscopes make objects look **bigger**.

Electron microscopes let you see things in **more** detail than light microscopes.

Electron microscopes have a **higher** resolution than light microscopes.

1 a)

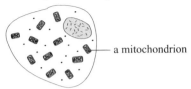
— a mitochondrion

[1 mark]

   b)   B *[1 mark]*

   c)   E.g. nucleus *[1 mark]*. This contains DNA that controls what the cell does *[1 mark]*.
Cell membrane *[1 mark]*. This controls what goes in and out of the cell / allows molecules to communicate with the cell *[1 mark]*.

2 a)   **J** — chromosomal DNA/chromosome *[1 mark]*
         K — plasmid *[1 mark]*

   b)   E.g. prokaryotic cells do not have a nucleus whereas eukaryotic cells do. / Prokaryotic cells contain plasmids, eukaryotic cells do not. / Prokaryotic cells don't contain mitochondria whereas eukaryotic cells do. *[1 mark]*

Page 3 — Light Microscopy

1 a)   B *[1 mark]*

   b)   **X** — Eyepiece lens *[1 mark]*
         Y — Stage *[1 mark]*
         Z — Lamp *[1 mark]*

   c) i)   × 4 *[1 mark]*

Remember, you should always start with the lowest-powered objective lens — this makes it easier to get your specimen into view.

       ii)   They bring the image into focus by moving the stage up and down *[1 mark]*.

      iii)   She should select the × 40 or × 10 objective lens *[1 mark]* and use the focusing knobs to bring the sample back into focus *[1 mark]*.

Page 4 — More on Light Microscopy

1 a)   (total magnification = eyepiece lens magnification × objective lens magnification)
         = 10 × 40 = **× 400** *[1 mark]*

   b)   A *[1 mark]*

If the total magnification is × 100, then the objective lens magnification must be 100 ÷ 10 = × 10.

2 a)   A *[1 mark]*

In this question you need to convert a smaller unit (μm) into a bigger unit (mm). This means you need to divide: 12 μm ÷ 1000 = 0.012 mm.

   b) i)   0.0074 × 1000 = **7.4 μm** *[1 mark]*
       ii)   7.4 μm × 1000 = **7400 nm** *[1 mark]*

Page 5 — DNA

Warm-up

polymer — a long chain of monomers
DNA — the genetic material of an organism
double helix — the spiral shape of a DNA molecule

1   B *[1 mark]*
2   C *[1 mark]*
3   RNA only has a single strand whereas DNA has two *[1 mark]*.

Page 6 — Enzymes

1 a)   active site *[1 mark]*
   b)   B *[1 mark]*

Remember, the substrate has to fit into the active site (like a key fitting into a lock).

2   A *[1 mark]*
3 a)   The rate of reaction in
         [1 mark].

   b)   The temperature is to
         been denatured / has
         no longer fits in the a..
         enzyme will no longer catalyse the reaction *[1 mark]*.

Page 7 — More on Enzymes

1   A *[1 mark]*
2 a)   optimum pH = 4.4 *[1 mark]*
   b)   C *[1 mark]*

A low pH affects the bonds holding the active site together, causing it to change shape.

Page 8 — Investigating Enzyme Activity

1 a)   two minutes = 120 seconds
         rate of reaction = 72 ÷ 120 = **0.6 cm³/second** *[2 marks for correct answer, otherwise 1 mark for correct working.]*

   b)   By putting them in a water bath *[1 mark]*.

   c)   The volume of product released in two minutes *[1 mark]*.

Remember, the dependent variable in an experiment is the thing that you measure.

   d)   Any two from: e.g. the concentration of substrate solution / the concentration of enzyme solution / the pH of the solutions. *[2 marks, 1 mark for each correct answer]*

   e)   E.g. using a gas syringe / using a measuring cylinder filled with water and turned upside down in a beaker of water *[1 mark]*.

   f)   She should add buffer solution with a different pH to each test tube *[1 mark]*. She should keep each test tube at the same temperature *[1 mark]*.

Page 9 — Respiration

Warm-up

Respiration transfers energy from the breakdown of **glucose**.
Respiration makes a substance called **ATP**.

1 a)   D *[1 mark]*
   b)   carbon dioxide / water *[1 mark]*
2 a)   The snail released carbon dioxide as it respired *[1 mark]*.
   b)   It will have decreased *[1 mark]* because the snail will have used up oxygen as it respired *[1 mark]*.

Page 10 — More on Respiration

1   B *[1 mark]*
2   D *[1 mark]*
3   Ethanol *[1 mark]* and carbon dioxide *[1 mark]*. This is because the cells will respire anaerobically as there is little or no oxygen available *[1 mark]*.

4 a)   **glucose** → ethanol (alcohol) + **carbon dioxide**
         [2 marks, 1 mark for each correct answer]

   b)   If there was oxygen in the container it could lead to the yeast respiring aerobically *[1 mark]*, meaning that ethanol/alcohol wouldn't be produced *[1 mark]*.

Page 11 — Biological Molecules

1   C *[1 mark]*
2   A — lipid *[1 mark]*, B — glycerol *[1 mark]*
3 a)   (simple) sugars *[1 mark]*
   b)   amino acids *[1 mark]*

Page 12 — Photosynthesis

Warm-up

carbon dioxide concentration, light intensity, temperature

1   A *[1 mark]*
2 a)   chloroplasts *[1 mark]*
   b)   **carbon dioxide** + water ⟶ glucose + **oxygen**
         [2 marks, 1 mark for each correct answer]
   c)   A *[1 mark]*

3 a) E.g. it is warmer in summer than in winter. / Light intensity is greater in summer than in winter. *[1 mark]*

b) A faster rate of photosynthesis means that more glucose is made by the plant *[1 mark]*. This means there is more glucose available to make larger molecules, which increases the plant's biomass *[1 mark]*.

Page 13 — Investigating Photosynthesis

1 a) Dependent variable — volume of oxygen produced in 10 minutes *[1 mark]*.
Independent variable — relative light intensity *[1 mark]*.

b) Any two from: e.g. carbon dioxide concentration in the water / temperature / the plant being used. *[2 marks — 1 mark for each correct answer]*

c) 6 *[1 mark]*

d) Repeat the experiment at least three times *[1 mark]* and check that the results are similar *[1 mark]*.

e) 1 hour = 60 minutes
60 minutes ÷ 10 minutes = 6
rate of reaction = 12 × 6 = **72 cm³/hour** *[2 marks for correct answer, otherwise 1 mark for correct working.]*

f) She could put the boiling tube containing the plant into water baths of different temperatures *[1 mark]* and keep the light intensity constant throughout the experiment *[1 mark]*.

Topic B2 — Scaling Up

Page 14 — The Cell Cycle and Mitosis

Warm-up
Cells in the body divide by mitosis so that **the body can grow**.

1 A *[1 mark]*

2 a) once *[1 mark]*
A cell only divides once during the cell cycle — this produces two new cells that can then begin the cell cycle again.

b)

The cell stops making proteins.	
The DNA is replicated.	✓
The cell grows.	✓
The cell structures are broken down.	

[1 mark]

c) The chromosomes are being pulled apart by cell fibres *[1 mark]*. The two arms of each chromosome go to opposite ends of the cell *[1 mark]*.

Page 15 — Cell Differentiation and Stem Cells

1 B *[1 mark]*

2 a) D *[1 mark]*

b) It allows organisms to work more efficiently *[1 mark]*.

c) Because embryonic stem cells have the potential to turn into any kind of cell at all *[1 mark]*, whereas adult stem cells are only able to turn into certain types of cell *[1 mark]*.

d) They are used to replace damaged cells *[1 mark]*.

Page 16 — Diffusion and Active Transport

1 a)

⟶ *[1 mark]*

Remember, molecules diffuse from an area of higher concentration (where there are more of them) to an area of lower concentration (where there are fewer of them).

b) They are too big to fit through the membrane *[1 mark]*.

2 a) C *[1 mark]*

b) The concentration of glucose is lower in the gut than in the blood *[1 mark]*, so active transport is needed to move the glucose molecules against the concentration gradient *[1 mark]*.

Page 17 — Osmosis

1 Osmosis is the movement of **water** *[1 mark]* molecules across a partially permeable membrane from an area of **higher** *[1 mark]* water concentration to an area of **lower** *[1 mark]* water concentration.

2 a) D *[1 mark]*.

b) It will decrease *[1 mark]* because the turnip cells have a higher water potential than the concentrated salt solution, so water will move into the cells by osmosis (down the water potential gradient) *[1 mark]*.

Remember, water molecules will always move from an area of higher water potential to an area of lower water potential.

Page 18 — Exchange of Materials

Warm-up
1 — blue whale, 2 — tiger, 3 — bacterium

1 a) D *[1 mark]*
The surface area of a cube is the area of one face (length × width) × the number of faces. So here it is (3 × 3) × 6 = 54 μm². The volume of a cube is just length × width × height (3 × 3 × 3 = 27 μm³ in this case).

b) A *[1 mark]*
The surface area of the cube is 24 μm² and the volume is 8 μm³. This gives the cube a surface area to volume ratio of 24 : 8. To get the answer here, you need to simplify the ratio by dividing both sides by the volume.

c) Any three from: e.g. oxygen / water / food / mineral ions *[3 marks]*

2 The Arctic hare *[1 mark]* because it is smaller than the polar bear *[1 mark]*. This means it will have a larger surface area to volume ratio, so it will lose heat the fastest *[1 mark]*.

Page 19 — Exchange Surfaces

1 a) A = carbon dioxide *[1 mark]*
B = oxygen *[1 mark]*

b) The gases only have to diffuse a short distance *[1 mark]*, so diffusion can happen quickly *[1 mark]*.

2 The flatworm has a high surface volume to area ratio so enough oxygen can diffuse across its outer surface to supply its volume *[1 mark]*. The beetle has a lower surface area to volume ratio, so diffusion across its surface to the cells deep inside its body is too slow *[1 mark]*. So the beetle needs a gas exchange system and a circulatory system to supply enough oxygen to all of its cells *[1 mark]*.

Page 20 — The Circulatory System

1 a) B *[1 mark]*

b) E.g.

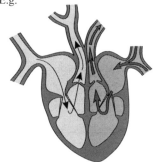

[1 mark for an arrow or arrows indicating the direction of blood flow into and out of the heart as shown.]

2 a) right atrium *[1 mark]*

b) How to grade your answer:
Level 0: There is no relevant information. *[No marks]*
Level 1: The answer gives a brief description of the journey blood takes through the double circulatory system, but does not include names of chambers or blood vessels of the heart. *[1 to 2 marks]*

Level 2:   The answer gives some description of the
           journey blood takes through the double
           circulatory system, and includes some names
           of the chambers and major blood vessels of the
           heart. *[3 to 4 marks]*

Level 3:   The answer gives a clear, detailed description
           of the journey blood takes through the double
           circulatory system and includes the names of the
           chambers and major blood vessels of the heart.
           [5 to 6 marks]

Here are some points your answer may include:
The deoxygenated blood is pumped from the right atrium
into the right ventricle.
The right ventricle pumps the blood out of the heart
through pulmonary artery.
The blood is pumped to the lungs, where it picks up oxygen.
The oxygenated blood flows into the heart through the
pulmonary vein.
It flows into the left atrium.
It is then pumped into the left ventricle.
The oxygenated blood is pumped out of the heart through
the aorta.
It is then travels round the whole body, before flowing back
to the vena cava in the heart.

Page 21 — The Blood Vessels

1   A *[1 mark]*, because e.g. it has much thicker walls than either
    B or C, so it's more likely to be an artery *[1 mark]*.
2 a)

Feature	Capillary	Artery	Vein
Lots of elastic fibres in blood vessel walls		✓	
Large lumen			✓
Thin, permeable walls	✓		
Valves			✓

[3 marks — 1 marks for each column in the table correctly filled in.]

b) To carry blood close to every cell in the body *[1 mark]*,
    so that substances can be exchanged with the cells *[1 mark]*.
c) Because they have different functions *[1 mark]*. Arteries
    carry blood away from the heart at high pressure, while veins
    carry blood back to the heart at a lower pressure *[1 mark]*.

Page 22 — The Blood

1 a) oxygen *[1 mark]*
  b) It gives a large surface area for absorbing oxygen *[1 mark]*.
  c) This increases the space available for carrying oxygen in the
      cell *[1 mark]*.
  d) E.g. they contain haemoglobin. / They are small/flexible
      [1 mark].
2 a) It transports substances around the body *[1 mark]*.
  b) $5000 \div 100 = 50$
      $50 \times 55 = $ **2750 cm³** *[2 marks for correct answer, otherwise
      1 mark for correct working.]*

Page 23 — Transport in Plants

Warm-up
A: phloem tube
B: xylem tube
1   C *[1 mark]*
2 a) water *[1 mark]*, mineral ions *[1 mark]*
  b) It gives the roots a large surface area to absorb substances
      [1 mark].

Page 24 — Transpiration and Stomata

1 a) The process by which water is lost from a plant is called
      transpiration *[1 mark]*. It is caused by the **evaporation**
      [1 mark] and diffusion of water from a plant's surface.
      The water loss creates a slight shortage of water in the plant,
      so more water is drawn up from the **roots** *[1 mark]*.
  b) mineral ions *[1 mark]*
2 a) X: stomata *[1 mark]*
      Y: guard cells *[1 mark]*
  b) When these cells are swollen, the stomata are open *[1 mark]*
      and water can diffuse out of the plant *[1 mark]*. When these
      cells are limp, the stomata are closed *[1 mark]* and very little
      water can escape *[1 mark]*.

Page 25 — Investigating Transpiration

1   high light intensity — It causes more stomata to open.
    [1 mark]
    high temperature — It increases the energy of water particles.
    [1 mark]
2 a) $2.0 + 1.8 + 2.3 + 1.9 + 1.7 = 9.7$
      $9.7 \div 5 = 1.94 = $ **1.9** (2 s.f.) *[2 marks for correct answer,
      otherwise 1 mark for mean = 1.94]*
  b) The greater the air flow around the plant, the greater the
      transpiration rate *[1 mark]*.
  c) E.g. increasing air flow means that more water vapour is
      swept away from the plant / increasing air flow reduces the
      concentration of water vapour outside the leaves *[1 mark]*.
      This increases the rate of diffusion of water out of the leaves
      [1 mark].

Topic B3 — Organism Level Systems

Page 26 — The Nervous System

Warm-up
Circled: Dropping a hot plate.
1   C *[1 mark]*
2 a) X — brain *[1 mark]*
      Y — spinal cord *[1 mark]*
  b) i) the central nervous system/CNS *[1 mark]*
     ii) It receives information from receptors *[1 mark]* and
         coordinates a response *[1 mark]*.
3

Stage	Number
An impulse is sent along a motor neurone.	4
Muscles in the eye respond to close the eyelid.	5
An impulse is sent along a sensory neurone.	2
A puff of air is detected by sensory receptors.	1
An impulse is sent along a relay neurone.	3

*[2 marks for all 5 stages in the correct order, otherwise
1 mark for 3 stages in the correct order.]*

Page 27 — Hormones

1   A *[1 mark]*
2 a) B *[1 mark]*
  b) B *[1 mark]*
  c) It will only affect (target) cells that have the right receptors to
      respond to that hormone *[1 mark]*.

Page 28 — The Menstrual Cycle

1 a) i) D *[1 mark]*
     ii) C *[1 mark]*
  b) It stops any of the eggs from maturing *[1 mark]*.
2   Y, because progesterone helps to maintain the uterus lining
    [1 mark] so the level of progesterone will be high while the
    uterus lining is being maintained *[1 mark]*. When the level
    falls, the uterus lining will break down and menstruation will
    occur *[1 mark]*.

Page 29 — Contraception

Warm-up

condom — non-hormonal

diaphragm — non-hormonal

mini-pill — hormonal

1 a) C *[1 mark]*

b) A *[1 mark]*

c) E.g. condoms protect against sexually transmitted infections (unlike the combined pill) *[1 mark]*. Condoms are unlikely to have unpleasant side-effects (there is a greater chance of these with the combined pill) *[1 mark]*.

d) E.g. condoms aren't as effective at preventing pregnancy as the combined pill *[1 mark]*. If using condoms, a couple has to think about contraception each time they have sex (unlike the combined pill) *[1 mark]*.

Page 30 — Controlling Blood Sugar Level

1 a) A *[1 mark]*

b) insulin *[1 mark]*

c) It makes sure that metabolic reactions happen at the correct rate *[1 mark]*.

2 a) i) D *[1 mark]*

ii) With insulin therapy/injections *[1 mark]*.

b) i) Any two from: e.g. eat a healthy diet. / Get regular exercise. / Lose weight if needed. / Drugs that improve the way the body's cells respond to insulin. *[2 marks — 1 mark for each correct answer.]*

ii) being overweight / obesity *[1 mark]*

Topic B4 — Community Level Systems

Page 31 — Ecosystems and Competition

1 a) C *[1 mark]*

b) B *[1 mark]*

2 a) Any two from: e.g. light / space / water / minerals/nutrients *[2 marks — 1 mark for each correct answer.]*

b) i) The population size of blackbirds might decrease *[1 mark]* as there would be less food for them to eat *[1 mark]*.

ii) Any two from: e.g. space / water / mates *[2 marks — 1 mark for each correct answer.]*

Page 32 — Abiotic and Biotic Factors

Warm-up

'availability of food' and 'predators' should be circled.

1 a) D *[1 mark]*

b) Any two from: e.g. moisture level / soil pH / light intensity / temperature *[2 marks — 1 mark for each correct answer.]*

2 a) A *[1 mark]*

A period of heavy rainfall means there will be lots of areas with plenty of water. This means there will be more areas where acacia trees can grow, so their population size may increase.

b) Prickly acacia trees may spread into areas that were too cold for them before *[1 mark]*.

Page 33 — Interactions Between Organisms

1 A *[1 mark]*

2 A *[1 mark]*

A mutualistic relationship is one where both organisms benefit.

3 How to grade your answer:

Level 0: There is no relevant information. *[No marks]*

Level 1: The answer describes the fluctuations in the population sizes of the snowshoe hare and the lynx but does not explain how the two are linked. *[1 to 2 marks]*

Level 2: The answer briefly explains the relationship between the population sizes of the snowshoe hare and the lynx, but some detail is missing. *[3 to 4 marks]*

Level 3: The answer gives a clear, detailed explanation of the relationship between the population sizes of the snowshoe hare and the lynx. *[5 to 6 marks]*

Here are some points your answer may include:

The graph shows that the lynx population grew after the snowshoe hare population increased.

This is because there was more food available for the lynx.

The graph also shows that when the population size of lynx was high, the population size of snowshoe hares fell.

This is because greater numbers of lynx meant that more snowshoe hares were eaten.

Once the population size of snowshoe hares had started falling, the population size of lynx also fell.

This was because there was less food available for the lynx.

Page 34 — Recycling and the Water Cycle

1 C *[1 mark]*

2 Microorganisms decay/decompose/break down the dead animals *[1 mark]*, meaning the materials they contain get put back into the soil *[1 mark]*.

3 a) evaporation *[1 mark]*

b) It provides fresh water for plants and animals *[1 mark]*.

Page 35 — The Carbon Cycle

1 D *[1 mark]*

2 a) Microorganisms break down animal waste *[1 mark]*. As they break it down, they release carbon dioxide back into the air through respiration *[1 mark]*.

b) Plants take in carbon dioxide from the air during photosynthesis *[1 mark]*. They use the carbon in carbon dioxide to make carbon compounds (e.g. carbohydrates) *[1 mark]*.

Page 36 — The Nitrogen Cycle

Warm-up

Plants need nitrogen so that they can make **proteins**.

1 a) B *[1 mark]*

b) By eating other organisms *[1 mark]*.

2 a) i) Any two from: e.g. plants / animals / bacteria *[2 marks — 1 mark for each correct answer.]*

ii) E.g. air *[1 mark]*, soil *[1 mark]*

b) Decomposers break down dead plants and animals/animal waste *[1 mark]*, which releases ammonia *[1 mark]*.

Topic B5 — Genes, Inheritance and Selection

Page 37 — Genes and Variation

1 C *[1 mark]*

2 a) B *[1 mark]*

b) Genes code for the production of proteins *[1 mark]*. Different proteins control the development of different characteristics *[1 mark]*.

c) An allele is a different version of a gene *[1 mark]* that gives a different form of a characteristic *[1 mark]*.

3 a) The characteristics that the organism shows *[1 mark]*.

b) The difference in weight must be caused by the environment *[1 mark]*, because the twins have exactly the same genes *[1 mark]*.

In this case, the environment can mean the amount of food each twin eats or the amount of exercise they each do.

Page 38 — More on Variation and Genetic Variants

1 A *[1 mark]*

2 B *[1 mark]*

CGP

GCSE
Combined Science
For OCR Gateway (Grade 9-1)

New!

Exam Practice Answer Book
Foundation Level

For the new course starting September 2016

Contents

Published by CGP

ISBN: 978 1 78294 524 6

www.cgpbooks.co.uk
Printed by Elanders Ltd, Newcastle upon Tyne.
Clipart from Corel®
Text, design, layout and original illustrations © Coordination Group Publications Ltd. (CGP) 2016
All rights reserved.

3   Length: The length of courgettes shows continuous variation *[1 mark]*. This is because courgette length varies within a range / there are no separate groups *[1 mark]*.
Colour: The colour of courgettes shows discontinuous variation *[1 mark]*. This is because courgette colour is divided into three separate groups *[1 mark]*.

Page 39 — Sexual Reproduction and Meiosis

1   D *[1 mark]*
2 a)   D *[1 mark]*
The diagram in the question shows a diploid cell. This cell contains two pairs of chromosomes before it undergoes meiosis. The first division causes these pairs to split up so that the two new cells only contain one chromosome from each pair. In the second division the chromosome in each cell is pulled apart so that each of the four gametes end up containing only one chromosome arm.
  b)   two *[1 mark]*
  c)   Four gametes are produced *[1 mark]*. Each gamete is haploid / only has half the number of chromosomes of normal cells *[1 mark]*. Each of the gametes is genetically different from the others *[1 mark]*.

Page 40 — Genetic Diagrams

Warm-up

heterozygous — Having two alleles the same for a particular gene.
homozygous — Having two different alleles for a particular gene.

1 a)

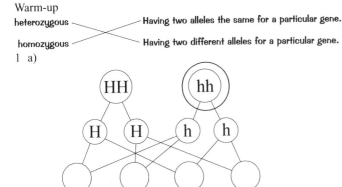

[1 mark]
  b)   Hh *[1 mark]*
  c)   The offspring all have short hair *[1 mark]*.
All the offspring have the genotype Hh. This means they all have the dominant allele (H), so they all have short hair.
2   No *[1 mark]*. The tall allele/T is dominant over the dwarf allele/t, so its presence will determine what characteristic is shown in the phenotype *[1 mark]*. A tall plant could have the alleles TT or Tt *[1 mark]*.

Page 41 — More Genetic Diagrams & Sex Determination

1 a)

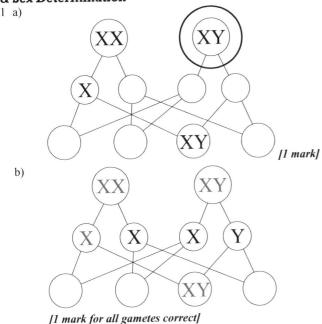

[1 mark]

  b)

[1 mark for all gametes correct]

c)

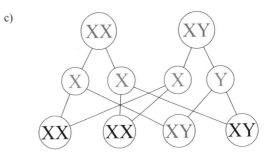

[1 mark if all the offspring genotypes are correct]
  d)   E.g. 1:1 *[1 mark]*
You could have also written 2:2 or even 50:50 here as your answer — all of these ratios show that there is an equal chance of the offspring being male or female.
2 a)

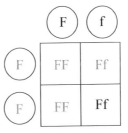

[1 mark for correct genotypes of gametes.
1 mark for correct genotype of offspring.]
  b)   half / 1 in 2 *[1 mark]*
  c)   0 out of 4 *[1 mark]*
Remember, cystic fibrosis is caused by a recessive allele, so two copies of the allele are needed for an individual to have it. None of the offspring in the genetic diagram have two copies so none of them have it.

Page 42 — Classification

Warm-up
kingdom, **phylum**, class, **order**, family, genus, **species**
1 a)   DNA sequencing *[1 mark]*
  b)   Organism F *[1 mark]* as its DNA has the highest percentage similarity (96%) to human DNA *[1 mark]*.
2 a)   The grouping of living organisms *[1 mark]* based on similarities and differences between them *[1 mark]*.
  b)   D *[1 mark]*

Page 43 — Evolution and Natural Selection

Warm-up
Evolution is the change in the inherited characteristics of a population over time, through the process of natural selection.
1   C *[1 mark]*
2   How to grade your answer:
  Level 0: There is no relevant information. *[No marks]*
  Level 1: There is a brief explanation of how a population of hares with large ears could have evolved, but key information is missing. *[1 to 2 marks]*
  Level 2: There is some explanation of how a population of hares with large ears could have evolved, but some detail is missing. *[3 to 4 marks]*
  Level 3: There is a full explanation of how a population of hares with large ears could have evolved.
  [5 to 6 marks]
Here are some points your answer may include:
The original population of hares would have had variation in the sizes of ears.
This variation would have been caused by the presence of genetic variants/alleles in the population.
Genetic variants/alleles are caused by mutations in DNA.
Hares with larger ears would lose more heat. This would make them more likely to survive and reproduce in the warm climate than hares with smaller ears. So the genetic variants/alleles for larger ears would be more likely to be passed on to offspring than genetic variants/alleles for smaller ears.

Over time, the genetic variants/alleles for larger ears would become more common in the population until all the hares in the population had larger ears.

Page 44 — Evidence for Evolution

1   C *[1 mark]*

2   Fossil A looks more similar to the modern human foot than Fossil B *[1 mark]*.

3   Going down the table: 4, 2, 1, 3 *[2 marks for all four stages in the correct order, otherwise 1 mark for two stages in the correct order.]*

Topic B6 — Global Challenges

Pages 45-46 — Investigating Distribution and Abundance

Warm-up

distribution — Where an organism is found in a habitat.

abundance — How many individuals are found in an area.

1   B *[1 mark]*

2 a)   E.g. a sweep net *[1 mark]*

   b)

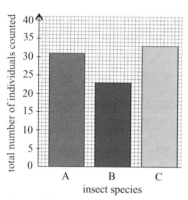

[1 mark for correctly drawn bars, 1 mark for sensibly labelled axes.]

3 a)   C *[1 mark]*

   b)   mean = total number of organisms ÷ number of quadrats

        = (26 + 23 + 18) ÷ 3 = 67 ÷ 3 = 22.33...

        = **22** (2 s.f.) *[2 marks for correct answer to 2 significant figures, otherwise 1 mark for mean = 22.33...]*

   c)   Yes. If you arrange the results from quadrats 1 to 3 in order from smallest to largest, then 14 is the middle value *[1 mark]*.

Watch out: you get the mark for your explanation here, not for just saying 'yes'.

   d)   E.g. yes, because the mean number of buttercups in Area 1 is lower than the mean number of buttercups in Area 2. / No, because there could be other factors affecting the growth of the buttercups that haven't been investigated *[1 mark]*.

Page 47 — Population Size

1 a)   total number of limpets = mean per quadrat × total area

        14 × 1750 = **24 500** limpets *[1 mark]*.

The size of the quadrat is 1 m² so all you have to do is multiply the mean number of limpets per quadrat by the total area of the beach.

   b)   1750 ÷ 0.25 = 7000

        7000 × 5 = **35 000** limpets *[2 marks for correct answer, otherwise 1 mark for correct working.]*

You could have also worked this answer out by finding the mean number of limpets per m² first (in each 0.25 m² quadrat there was a mean of 5 limpets — 1 ÷ 0.25 = 4, so in 1 m² there would be a mean of 4 × 5 = 20 limpets). Then you just need to multiply this number by the area of the beach (20 × 1750 = 35 000 limpets).

2 a)   Firstly, they should have captured a sample of the snail population *[1 mark]*. They should have marked these snails *[1 mark]* then released all of them back into the pond *[1 mark]*. After some time, they should have recaptured another sample of the snails and counted how many of this sample were marked *[1 mark]*.

   b)   E.g. made sure the marks didn't harm the snails. / Handled the snails carefully. / Made sure all the snails were returned to the pond. *[1 mark]*

   c)   E.g. that marking the snails didn't affect their chance of survival. / That the marks didn't wash off the snails. *[1 mark]*

Page 48 — Using Keys and Factors Affecting Distribution

1   C *[1 mark]*, because its wings have spots and stripes *[1 mark]*.

2 a)   Record the pH of the soil at the different sample sites *[1 mark]*.

By recording the pH of the soil as well as the number of dandelions in each quadrat, the students would be able to look for any patterns in their data, e.g. whether more or fewer dandelions were found in areas with a low pH.

   b)   e.g. light intensity / temperature / soil moisture *[1 mark]*

Page 49 — Using Transects

1 a)   B and C *[1 mark]*

   b)   A *[1 mark]*

   c)   E.g. a quadrat / a tape measure *[1 mark]*

2   56 squares are more than half covered by the grass species = **56%** *[1 mark]*

You should count a square if it's more than half covered.

Page 50 — Human Impacts on Ecosystems

Warm-up

Biodiversity is the **variety** of living organisms in an ecosystem.

If the number of species in an area decreases, the biodiversity of the area **decreases**.

Humans **can** affect biodiversity.

1   B *[1 mark]*

2 a)   Any two from: e.g. building / farming / dumping waste / quarrying *[2 marks — 1 mark for each correct answer]*.

   b)   It decreases the biodiversity of plant species *[1 mark]*.

   c)   It is likely to decrease the biodiversity of animal species *[1 mark]*. This is because cutting the woodland down is likely to destroy the habitat of many animals *[1 mark]* meaning they die / have to move somewhere else *[1 mark]*.

Page 51 — More Human Impacts on Ecosystems

1   It means the hedgehogs will have somewhere to live / it helps to protect hedgehogs' habitat *[1 mark]*.

2   C *[1 mark]*

3 a)   Hunting could lead to the extinction of orangutans, which would decrease the biodiversity in rainforests *[1 mark]*.

   b)   In the zoo the animals are protected from hunting *[1 mark]*, which helps to protect the species from becoming extinct *[1 mark]*.

   c)   By protecting the habitat of local species *[1 mark]*.

Page 52 — Maintaining Biodiversity

1   C *[1 mark]*

2 a)   E.g. by bringing more money to the area *[1 mark]*.

   b)   E.g. if an area is protected, the undiscovered species of plants are less likely to become extinct *[1 mark]*.

3 a)   E.g. it helps to make sure that humans will have enough tuna to eat in the future *[1 mark]*.

   b)   E.g. it may have been hard to get all countries that fish for bluefin tuna to work together / sign up to an agreement *[1 mark]*.

   c)   E.g. it may be hard to keep track of how many bluefin tuna are being caught by different countries *[1 mark]*.

Page 53 — Selective Breeding

1   A *[1 mark]*

Selective breeding is used to create different varieties of the same species. It can't be used to introduce genetic material from another organism, such as a gene from a human into a bacterium — for this you would need to use genetic engineering techniques.

2 a) When humans choose which plants or animals are going to breed *[1 mark]*.
  b) B and D *[1 mark]*
  c) E.g. to get cows that produce more milk *[1 mark]*.

3   From the existing stock, organisms that have the required feature are selected and bred together *[1 mark]*. The best of the offspring are selected and bred together *[1 mark]*. This process is continued over several generations *[1 mark]*.

Page 54 — Genetic Engineering

1 a) It has had genes from another organism inserted into its genome *[1 mark]*.
  b) C *[1 mark]*

2 a) E.g. it can be hard to predict how changing an animal's genome will affect the animal. / Many genetically modified embryos don't survive. / Some genetically modified animals suffer from health problems later in life *[1 mark]*.
  b) E.g. genes used in genetic engineering may get out into the environment. / Some people worry that GM crops might have a negative effect on food chains/human health *[1 mark]*.

3 a) Whether a GM crop affects the number of wild flowers growing in a nearby area *[1 mark]*.
  b) E.g. they could repeat their experiment with other meadows *[1 mark]*.

Page 55 — Health and Disease

1 a) A condition that stops an organism working as well as it should *[1 mark]*.
  b) i) A disease that can spread between organisms *[1 mark]*.
    ii) Any three from: e.g. they can't be passed from one organism to another. / They generally last for a long time. / They generally progress slowly. / They are often linked to unhealthy lifestyles. *[3 marks — 1 mark for each correct answer]*

2 a) The immune system would normally protect a person from developing tuberculosis *[1 mark]* but HIV stops the immune system from working properly *[1 mark]*.
  b) HPV can infect the reproductive system and cause cervical cancer *[1 mark]*. Since the vaccine protects girls against infection by the HPV virus, it can prevent them from getting cervical cancers caused by HPV *[1 mark]*.

Pages 56-57 — How Disease Spreads

Warm-up

Viruses — These pathogens are not cells. They copy themselves inside the infected organism's cells.
Protists — Many of the pathogens in this category are parasites.
Fungi — Some of these pathogens produce spores so they can spread.
Bacteria — These pathogens produce toxins that damage your cells and tissues, making you feel ill.

1 a) B *[1 mark]*
  b) A *[1 mark]*
2 a) sexually transmitted infection/disease *[1 mark]*
  b) late stage HIV / AIDS *[1 mark]*
3 a) fungus *[1 mark]*
  b) Fungal spores from an infected plant can blow in the wind to other plants *[1 mark]*.
4 a) tobacco mosaic virus/TMV *[1 mark]*
  b) Tobacco mosaic virus/TMV is spread when infected leaves rub against healthy ones *[1 mark]*. Not all of the farmer's plants are in contact with infected leaves *[1 mark]*.
5   E.g. eating contaminated food *[1 mark]*, touching contaminated surfaces *[1 mark]*.

Page 58 — Reducing and Preventing the Spread of Disease

1 a) E.g. they can be killed / their habitats can be destroyed to stop them from breeding *[1 mark]*.
  b) Any two from: e.g. by controlling the movement of plant materials. / By destroying infected plants. / By chemical control *[2 marks — 1 mark for each correct answer]*.

2 a) A tissue will catch the droplets, so other people don't breathe them in *[1 mark]*.
  b) E.g. by using simple hygiene measures (such as washing your hands before making food) / by isolating infected individuals / by vaccinating people against the disease. *[1 mark]*

3   E.g. he could test the sample to see if the DNA of *Erysiphe graminis* is present *[1 mark]*. He could test the sample to see if antigens for *Erysiphe graminis* are present *[1 mark]*.

Page 59 — The Human Immune System

1   A *[1 mark]*
2   It stops pathogens from getting inside the body *[1 mark]*. It also releases substances that kill pathogens *[1 mark]*.
3   How to grade your answer:
    Level 0: There is no relevant information. *[No marks]*
    Level 1: There is a brief mention of how either platelets or white blood cells defend the body against pathogens. *[1 to 2 marks]*
    Level 2: There is some explanation of how platelets and white blood cells defend the body against pathogens. *[3 to 4 marks]*
    Level 3: There is a detailed explanation of how platelets and white blood cells defend the body against pathogens. *[5 to 6 marks]*

Here are some points your answer may include:
Platelets:
If a blood vessel is damaged, platelets (tiny bits of cells) in the blood clump together.
This 'plugs' the damaged area. This is known as blood clotting.
It stops pathogens from entering the wound.
White blood cells:
Some white blood cells contain lots of enzymes and can change shape.
This lets them engulf pathogens and digest them — this is called phagocytosis.
Some white blood cells can produce antibodies that recognise specific antigens on pathogens and lock on to them.
These antibodies make sure the pathogens can be found and engulfed by other white blood cells.
Some white blood cells (called memory cells) stay around in the blood after the pathogen has been fought off. This means that if the person is infected with the same pathogen again they can quickly produce the antibodies to help kill the pathogen.
Some white blood cells can produce antitoxins that stop toxins produced by invading bacteria from causing harm.

Page 60 — Vaccinations and Medicines

Warm-up
To stop them getting ill in the future.
1   an antiseptic *[1 mark]*
2   Yes, because antibiotics don't kill viruses *[1 mark]*.
3   Antibody production after infection in the vaccinated child happens much faster than in the unvaccinated child *[1 mark]* and more antibodies are also produced *[1 mark]*.

Page 61 — Investigating Antimicrobials

1 a)   D *[1 mark]*
   b)   C *[1 mark]*

The pale areas around the discs show the clear zones (places where the bacteria has been killed). The clear zone around disc B is larger than the clear zone around disc A. This shows that antibiotic B was more effective than antibiotic A.

   c) i)   It could affect the results of the investigation. / It could result in the growth of pathogens *[1 mark]*.
      ii)   Any two from: e.g. regularly disinfect work surfaces. / Sterilise equipment before and after use. / Work near a Bunsen flame. / Briefly flame the neck of the glass container of bacteria just after it's opened and just before it's closed. *[2 marks — 1 mark for each correct answer.]*

Page 62 — Comparing Antimicrobials

1 a)   radius of D = 30.20 ÷ 2 = 15.10 mm
        area of D = 3.14×15.10^2 = **716.0 mm^2** (4 s.f.)

If you use the π button on your calculator, you'll get a slightly different area of 716.3.

      [2 marks for correct answer, otherwise 1 mark for correct calculation of radius.]

Remember that the radius of a circle is half its diameter. So, for the calculation of the area of the clear zone you have to divide the diameter you have been given by 2.

   b) i)   D *[1 mark]*
      ii)   E.g. an incorrect measurement / not as much antibiotic soaked into the paper disc / the antibiotic concentration was lower for this plate *[1 mark]*.

An anomalous result is a result that doesn't fit in with the others. For this question you just need to give a sensible suggestion of something that might have gone wrong in the investigation that could have caused the anomalous value.

Page 63 — Developing New Medicines

1 a) i)   C *[1 mark]*
      ii)   Any two from: computer models / human cells / human tissues / animals *[2 marks — 1 mark for each correct answer]*.
   b)   healthy volunteers *[1 mark]*
2 a)   A substance that looks like the drug being tested but doesn't do anything *[1 mark]*.
   b)   So that doctors are able to compare the two groups *[1 mark]* to see if the drug makes a real difference to their condition *[1 mark]*.
   c)   D *[1 mark]*

Pages 64-65 — Non-Communicable Diseases

Warm-up
true, true, false, true

1   C *[1 mark]*

Remember, communicable diseases can be spread between organisms. Non-communicable diseases can't.

2 a)   It is something that increases a person's chance of getting a disease *[1 mark]*.
   b)   E.g. drinking too much alcohol *[1 mark]*.
   c)   C *[1 mark]*
3 a)   D *[1 mark]*
   b)   E.g. smoking / obesity / drinking too much alcohol *[1 mark]*.
4 a)   Patient D's BMI value indicates that they are moderately obese *[1 mark]* whereas the other patients are classed as 'overweight' or 'normal' *[1 mark]*.
   b)   No, because obesity is only a risk factor for cardiovascular disease, so it doesn't mean they will definitely develop the disease *[1 mark]*.
   c)   Any two from: e.g. a lack of exercise / eating a diet containing too much fat / smoking. / drinking too much alcohol *[2 marks — 1 mark for each correct answer]*.

Page 66 — Treating Cardiovascular Disease

Warm-up
Cardiovascular diseases are diseases of the **heart/blood vessels** and of the **blood vessels/heart**. An example of a cardiovascular disease is **coronary heart disease**.

1

	Eat a diet that is high in fat.
✓	Stop smoking.
✓	Exercise regularly.
	Drink more alcohol.

   [1 mark]

2 a)   E.g. a stent could be inserted *[1 mark]*. / He could have coronary bypass surgery *[1 mark]*.
   b)   Any two from: e.g. there is a risk of infection. / There is a risk of bleeding. / There is a risk of developing blood clots. *[2 marks — 1 mark for each correct answer]*.
   c)   Any two from: e.g. statins / anticoagulants / antihypertensives *[2 marks — 1 mark for each correct answer]*.

Page 67 — Stem Cells in Medicine

1 a)   B *[1 mark]*
   b)   A *[1 mark]*
2 a)   rejection *[1 mark]*
   b)   There may be less risk of rejection/the cells being attacked by the patient's immune system because the cells will be recognised by the body *[1 mark]*.
   c)   E.g. because after embryonic stem cells are removed, the embryo is destroyed *[1 mark]*. Some people believe that human embryos shouldn't be used in this way because each one is a potential human life *[1 mark]*.

Page 68 — Using Genome Research in Medicine

Warm-up
The genome is **the entire genetic material of an organism.**

1 a) i)   E.g. follow any lifestyle advice that will help to lower his risk *[1 mark]*.
      ii)   Any two from: e.g. knowing he has the gene may make him feel stressed. / He may come under pressure not to have children. / It could lead to him being discriminated against by employers. *[2 marks — 1 mark for each correct answer]*.
   b)   The new drugs can help to treat cancer by targeting the genes responsible for the cancer *[1 mark]*.

Topic C1 — Particles

Page 69 — States of Matter
Warm-up

  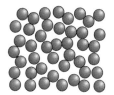

solid   gas   liquid

1 a) solid (strongest) → liquid → gas (weakest) *[1 mark]*
   b) condensation *[1 mark]*
   c) The hotter the liquid gets, the faster the particles will move *[1 mark]*.
2 When a physical change occurs, no new substances are made *[1 mark]*. During a chemical change, the atoms are rearranged to form new products *[1 mark]*.

Page 70 — The History of The Atom
1 A *[1 mark]*
2 a) Thomson *[1 mark]*
   b) Plum pudding model — A positively charged 'ball' with negatively charged electrons in it *[1 mark]*.
   Rutherford's nuclear model — A small positively charged nucleus surrounded by a 'cloud' of negative electrons *[1 mark]*.
3 a) E.g. both models have a positively charged nucleus at the centre of the atom *[1 mark]*.
   b) E.g. in Rutherford's model the electrons are in a cloud around the nucleus, but in Bohr's model they move around the nucleus in fixed shells *[1 mark]*.

Page 71 — The Atom
Warm-up
Protons (or **Neutrons**) and **neutrons** (or **protons**) are found in the nucleus of an atom. The nucleus has a **positive** charge. **Electrons** move around the nucleus in shells.
1 a) The distance from the centre of the atom/nucleus to the outer edge *[1 mark]*.
   b) C *[1 mark]*
2 a)

Particle	Relative Mass	Relative charge
proton	1	+1
neutron	1	0
electron	0.0005	**−1**

[1 mark for each row correctly completed.]
   b) Protons and neutrons are much heavier than electrons *[1 mark]*. The nucleus of the atom is where the protons and neutrons are found *[1 mark]*.

Page 72 — Atomic Numbers and Mass Numbers
1 a) How many protons there are in the atom *[1 mark]*.
   b) The total number of protons and neutrons in the atom *[1 mark]*.
2 a) 13 *[1 mark]*
   b) Mass number =13 + 14 = **27** *[1 mark]*
3 a) 6 *[1 mark]*
   b) Number of neutrons = 20 − 10 = **10** *[1 mark]*
   c) 9 *[1 mark]*

Page 73 — Ions and Isotopes
1 C *[1 mark]*
2 a) Number of electrons = 35 + 1 = **36** *[1 mark]*
   b) Number of electrons = 24 − 3 = **21** *[1 mark]*

3 a) 29 *[1 mark]*
   b) 63 − 29 = **34** *[1 mark]*
   c) 65 − 29 = **36** *[1 mark]*

Topic C2 — Elements, Compounds and Mixtures

Page 74 — The Periodic Table
1 a) By atomic number *[1 mark]*.
   b) Mendeleev put the elements in order of atomic mass *[1 mark]*. He left gaps and swapped the positions of some elements so that he could keep elements with similar properties in the same column *[1 mark]*.
   c) B *[1 mark]*
2 a) Period: 3 *[1 mark]*.
   Reason: Element Q has 3 shells of electrons *[1 mark]*.
   b) Group: 2 *[1 mark]*.
   Reason: Element R has 2 electrons in its outer shell *[1 mark]*.

Page 75 — Electron Shells
1

Electron shell	Number of electrons it can hold
1st	**2**
2nd	**8**
3rd	**8**

[3 marks — 1 mark for each correct answer]
2 C *[1 mark]*
3 a) 2.8.7 *[1 mark]*
   b)

[1 mark for total number of electrons being correct, 1 mark for correct number of electrons in each shell.]
You don't have to have shown the electrons in pairs — as long as you've put the right number of electrons in each shell you get the mark.
   c) 2.8.5 *[1 mark]*

Page 76 — Simple Ions
1 a) Ions are formed when atoms lose or gain electrons *[1 mark]*.
   b) 3 *[1 mark]*
   c) 2− *[1 mark]*
2 a) D *[1 mark]*
   b) A^+ — A metal from Group 1
   D^- — A non-metal from Group 7
   X^{2+} — A metal from Group 2
   Z^{2-} — A non-metal from Group 6
   [2 marks if all four correct, otherwise 1 mark if two correct]

Page 77 — Ionic Bonding
1 a) Mg^{2+} *[1 mark]*
   O^{2-} *[1 mark]*
   b) $MgBr_2$ *[1 mark]*
2 a)

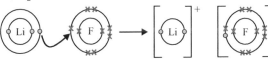

[1 mark for arrow showing electron transfer from Li to F, 1 mark for correct charges on both ions, 1 mark for adding one dot to complete the outer shell of the fluoride ion.]
   b) electrostatic attraction / electrostatic force *[1 mark]*
   c) Li_2O *[1 mark]*.

Page 78 — Ionic Compounds

Warm-up

In an ionic compound, the particles are held together by **strong** forces of attraction. These forces are called ionic bonds and act **in all directions**.

1 a)   E.g.

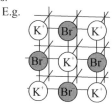

[1 mark for correct structure, with alternating ions]

You'd also get the mark if you labelled all the white circles as Br⁻ and all the grey circles as K⁺.

b)   E.g. the diagram doesn't correctly represent the sizes of ions / it shows gaps between the ions *[1 mark]*.

2 a)   Sodium bromide has strong attractions between its ions *[1 mark]*, so it takes a lot of energy to separate the ions *[1 mark]*.

b)   When sodium bromide is a solid, its ions are fixed in place, so they can't move *[1 mark]*. When it is in solution, the ions separate and are free to move, so a current can flow *[1 mark]*.

Page 79 — Covalent Bonding

1 a)

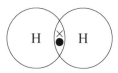

[1 mark]

b)

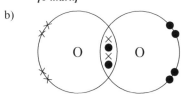

[1 mark]

2 a)

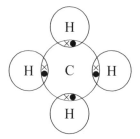

*[1 mark for the correct layout of atoms and shells,
1 mark for the correct number of electrons in each bond]*

b)   There is a strong attraction between the positive nuclei of the atoms and the negative electrons in each shared pair *[1 mark]*.

Page 80 — Simple Molecules

1 a)   The bonds between the atoms are strong *[1 mark]*.
       The forces between the molecules are weak *[1 mark]*.

b)   To melt a simple molecular substance you need to break the forces of attraction between the molecules *[1 mark]*. These forces are very weak, so it doesn't take much energy to break them *[1 mark]*.

2 a) i)   ball and stick model *[1 mark]*

   ii)   displayed formula *[1 mark]*

b)   E.g. the diagram shows gaps between the atoms, but in reality these spaces are filled by the atoms' electron clouds. *[1 mark for any sensible limitation of ball and stick models.]*

Page 81 — Giant Covalent Structures and Fullerenes

1   fullerene *[1 mark]*

2 a)   four *[1 mark]*

b)   Diamond does not have any free electrons or ions *[1 mark]*.

c)   To melt diamond you have to break the strong covalent bonds holding the atoms together *[1 mark]* which takes a lot of energy *[1 mark]*.

d)   Each carbon atom forms three covalent bonds *[1 mark]*, creating sheets of carbon atoms/rings/hexagons *[1 mark]*.

e)   Each carbon atom in graphite has one electron that's free to move *[1 mark]*. This means that graphite can conduct electricity *[1 mark]*.

Page 82 — Polymers and Properties of Materials

Warm-up

In a polymer, lots of **small** units are joined together to form a **long** molecule.

1 a)   The melting point is determined by the structure and bonding of the material, not by the individual atoms it contains *[1 mark]*.

b)   covalent bonds *[1 mark]*

2 a)   The melting point of polymers is determined by the strength of the forces between the different polymer chains *[1 mark]*.

b)   E.g. polymer A may have covalent bonds/cross-links between the chains / polymer A may have stronger bonds/forces between the chains than polymer B *[1 mark]*.

Page 83 — Metals

Warm-up

The following should be circled: copper, tin, magnesium, aluminium.

1 a)   electrons *[1 mark]*

b)   There are strong forces of attraction between the positive metal ions and the negative electrons *[1 mark]*.

c)   Metallic bonds are very strong *[1 mark]* so lots of energy is needed to break them *[1 mark]*.

d)   From top to bottom of the table: true, false, true, false *[4 marks — 1 mark for each correct answer]*.

e)   An alloy *[1 mark]*.

Page 84 — States, Structure and Bonding

1   B *[1 mark]*

2 a)   sodium chloride *[1 mark]*

At 900 °C, water would be a gas and copper would be a solid.

b)   Sodium chloride *[1 mark]* and water *[1 mark]*.

At 1500 °C, copper would be a liquid.

3   Substance C *[1 mark]* because it has a high melting point and boiling point *[1 mark]* and only conducts electricity when molten *[1 mark]*.

Page 85 — Purity

Warm-up

an alloy — impure

diamond — pure

sea water — impure

carbon dioxide gas — pure

1   The scientific definition of a pure substance is one that contains only one element or compound *[1 mark]*. Although it is labelled 'pure', Stanley's spring water probably contains traces of other compounds/elements as well as water molecules (so it does not fit the scientific definition of 'pure water') *[1 mark]*.

2 a)   Sample A *[1 mark]* because it melted at a specific temperature whereas sample B melted over a range of temperatures / sample A melted at a higher temperature than sample B *[1 mark]*.

b)   A *[1 mark]*.

Page 86 — Simple Distillation

1 a) condenser *[1 mark]*
  b) E.g. the thermometer will read 56 °C *[1 mark]*.
  c) The solution in the flask is heated and the propanone evaporates *[1 mark]*. The vapour passes into the condenser where it cools and condenses *[1 mark]*. The pure liquid propanone flows into the beaker where it is collected *[1 mark]*. The impurity has a higher boiling point than propanone, so it stays in the flask *[1 mark]*.
  d) E.g. electric heater / water bath *[1 mark]*

You shouldn't use a Bunsen burner because it could cause the liquid to catch fire.

Page 87 — Fractional Distillation

1 a) A mixture of liquids *[1 mark]* with similar boiling points *[1 mark]*.
  b) fractionating column *[1 mark]*
  c) The fractionating column is cooler at the top than the bottom *[1 mark]* so substance X will condense before it reaches the top of the column *[1 mark]*. It will then run back down into the flask *[1 mark]*.
  d) fraction *[1 mark]*

Page 88 — Filtration and Crystallisation

1 a) filtration *[1 mark]*
  b) A *[1 mark]*
2 a) crystallisation *[1 mark]*
  b) How to grade your answer:
  Level 0: Nothing written worthy of credit *[No marks]*.
  Level 1: A brief method is given, but there are steps missing *[1 to 2 marks]*.
  Level 2: A fairly complete method is given, but it is lacking in detail, or steps are out of order *[3 to 4 marks]*.
  Level 3: A full, clear and detailed method is given *[5 to 6 marks]*.
  Here are some points your answer may include:
  Put the calcium chloride solution in the evaporating dish.
  Place the tripod on a heatproof mat. Put the gauze on the tripod, and put the evaporating dish on the gauze.
  Using a Bunsen burner, gently heat the solution in the evaporating.
  Stop heating once about half of the solvent has evaporated (or when crystals start to form).
  Leave the solution to cool until crystals have formed.
  Put the filter paper in the funnel and place the funnel in a beaker.
  Pour the mixture into the filter paper.
  The liquid will pass through the filter paper, but the solid crystals will be left behind on the filter paper.
  After all the liquid has passed through the filter paper leave the crystals to dry out.

Page 89 — Chromatography

1 a) B *[1 mark]*
  b) Pencil marks are insoluble (so won't dissolve into the solvent) *[1 mark]*.
2 a) solvent front *[1 mark]*
  b) The different dyes in the ink move up the paper at different speeds / they spend different amounts of time in the mobile and stationary phases *[1 mark]*.
  c) silica gel *[1 mark]*

Page 90 — Interpreting Chromatograms

1 D *[1 mark]*
2 a) D *[1 mark]*
  b) C *[1 mark]*
  c) R_f = distance moved by substance ÷ distance moved by solvent
  $R_f = 9.0 \div 12.0 = \mathbf{0.75}$
  [2 marks for correct answer, otherwise 1 mark for using the correct formula to calculate R_f.]

Page 91 — Relative Masses

1 a) relative formula mass of HCl = 35.5 + 1.0 = **36.5** *[1 mark]*
  b) relative formula mass of Cl_2 = 35.5 + 35.5 = **71** *[1 mark]*
2 B *[1 mark]*
3 a) $M_r(MgSO_4)$ = 24.3 + 32.1 + (16.0 × 4) = **120.4** *[1 mark]*
  b) $M_r(Mg(OH)_2)$ = 24.3 + [(16.0 + 1.0) × 2] = **58.3** *[1 mark]*

Page 92 — Molecular and Empirical Formulas

Warm-up
oxygen: 2, carbon: 5, nitrogen: 0, hydrogen: 10
1 D *[1 mark]*
2 a) $H_2S_2O_6$ *[1 mark]*
  b) The largest number that goes into all the numbers in the molecular formula exactly is 2:
  H: 2 ÷ 2 = 1
  S: 2 ÷ 2 = 1
  O: 6 ÷ 2 = 3
  So the empirical formula is HSO_3 *[1 mark]*.

Topic C3 — Chemical Reactions

Page 93 — Conservation of Mass

1 a) The mass of the products will be the same as the mass of the reactants *[1 mark]*.
  b) C *[1 mark]*.
2 Disagree. Atoms are not created during a reaction *[1 mark]*. The extra mass came from the oxygen in the air becoming part of the solid product *[1 mark]*.
3 a) Total mass of reactants = 80.0 + 73.0 = 153 g
  Mass of sodium chloride = 153 − 36.0 = **117 g**
  [2 marks for correct answer, otherwise 1 mark for finding the total mass of the reactants.]
  b) M_r reactants = M_r NaOH + M_r HCl
  = 40 + 36.5 = 76.5
  M_r products = M_r NaCl + M_r H_2O
  = 58.5 + 18 = 76.5
  [1 mark for finding the total M_r of the reactants and 1 mark for finding the total M_r of the products.]

Page 94 — Chemical Formulas

Warm-up
2+ = magnesium, barium   1+ = lithium, potassium
1− = iodine, chlorine   2− = sulfur
1 C *[1 mark]*
2 3+ *[1 mark]*
Each chloride ion has a charge of 1−. There are three chloride ions for every one iron ion, so for each iron ion, there's a charge of (−1 × 3 =) −3 from chloride ions. Ionic compounds are neutral, so the iron ion must have a charge of 3+ to balance the charge from the chloride ions.
3 B *[1 mark]*

Page 95 — Chemical Equations

Warm-up
1) True   2) False   3) True   4) True
1 a) potassium hydroxide + **hydrobromic acid** → **potassium bromide + water** *[1 mark]*
  b) D *[1 mark]*
2 a) calcium carbonate *[1 mark]*, nitric acid *[1 mark]*
  b) $CaCO_3(s) + 2HNO_3(aq) \rightarrow Ca(NO_3)_2(aq) + H_2O(l) + CO_2(g)$ *[1 mark]*

Page 96 — Balancing Chemical Equations

1 C *[1 mark]*
2 a) D *[1 mark]*
  b) $4Na + O_2 \rightarrow 2Na_2O$ *[1 mark]*
3 a) $CH_4 + 2O_2 \rightarrow CO_2 + 2H_2O$ *[1 mark for correct reactants and products, 1 mark for correct balancing.]*
  b) $2CH_3OH + 3O_2 \rightarrow 2CO_2 + 4H_2O$ *[1 mark for correct reactants and products, 1 mark for correct balancing.]*

Page 97 — Endothermic and Exothermic Reactions

1 a) The reaction decreased the temperature of the surroundings *[1 mark]*.

 b) Energy is transferred from the surroundings *[1 mark]* to the reaction mixture *[1 mark]*.

2 a) The smallest amount of energy needed to start a reaction *[1 mark]*.

 b)

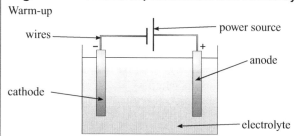

[1 mark]

 c) Exothermic *[1 mark]*. The products have less energy than the reactants *[1 mark]*.

 d) The temperature of the surroundings will increase *[1 mark]*.

Page 98 — Acids and Bases

Warm-up

Substances with a pH of less than 7 are **acids**. Substances with a pH of more than 7 are **bases**. Substances with a pH of 7 are **neutral**.

1 a) bicarbonate of soda / soap *[1 mark]*

 b) hydroxide/OH^- ion *[1 mark]*

2 a) A *[1 mark]*

 b) $H^+ + OH^- \rightarrow H_2O$ *[1 mark]*

 c) E.g. the solution will start red *[1 mark]*. As she adds the alkali it will gradually change colour/change to orange, then yellow *[1 mark]*. At the end of the reaction it will be green *[1 mark]*.

 d) E.g. using a pH probe *[1 mark]*.

Page 99 — Reactions of Acids

1 Hydrochloric acid — chloride
Nitric acid — nitrate
Sulfuric acid — sulfate
[1 mark for all three correct]

2 a) D *[1 mark]*

 b) carbon dioxide *[1 mark]*

3 a) zinc sulfate *[1 mark]*

 b) Difference: e.g. they produce different salts *[1 mark]*.
Similarity: e.g. they both produce hydrogen / a salt *[1 mark]*.

 c) $ZnCO_3 + H_2SO_4 \rightarrow ZnSO_4 + H_2O + CO_2$
[1 mark for correct products, 1 mark for correct reactants.]

Page 100 — Neutralisation Reactions

1 a)

		Acid	
		Hydrochloric acid	**Sulfuric acid**
Metal hydroxide	**Calcium hydroxide**	Calcium chloride	**Calcium sulfate**
	Copper hydroxide	**Copper chloride**	**Copper sulfate**

[2 marks for all three answers correct, otherwise 1 mark for any two answers correct.]

 b) hydrochloric acid + calcium hydroxide
$\rightarrow$ calcium chloride + water *[1 mark]*

 c) $Ca(OH)_2 + 2HCl \rightarrow CaCl_2 + 2H_2O$
[1 mark for formulas of both products correct, 1 mark for correct balancing.]

2 a) He will end up with a mixture of the salt and the acid *[1 mark]*.

 b) Put a measured amount of potassium hydroxide solution in a flask *[1 mark]*. Add a few drops of single indicator/ phenolphthalein/litmus *[1 mark]*. Use a burette to gradually add sulfuric acid to the alkali until the solution has been neutralised / until the indicator changes colour *[1 mark]*. Record how much sulfuric acid was added *[1 mark]*.

 c) potassium sulfate *[1 mark]* and water *[1 mark]*.

Page 101 — Making Salts

Warm-up

Mix two soluble salts together.

1 D *[1 mark]*

2 a) zinc chloride *[1 mark]*

 b) How to grade your answer:
Level 0: Nothing written worthy of credit *[No marks]*.
Level 1: A brief method is given, but there are steps missing *[1 to 2 marks]*.
Level 2: A full method is given, but it is lacking in detail, or steps are out of order *[3 to 4 marks]*.
Level 3: A full, clear and detailed method is given *[5 to 6 marks]*.
Here are some points your answer may include:
Warm the acid carefully.
Add the zinc oxide to hydrochloric acid.
When all the acid has been neutralised the excess metal oxide will sink to the bottom.
Filter the excess solid from the solution using a filter funnel and filter paper.
Heat the zinc chloride solution to evaporate some of the water.
Leave the solution to cool and form crystals.
Filter off the crystals using a filter funnel and filter paper.
Dry the crystals.

Page 102 — Oxidation, Reduction and Electrolysis

Warm-up

1 A *[1 mark]*

2 a) Reduction is the loss of oxygen from a compound *[1 mark]*.

 b) Substance: carbon / C *[1 mark]*
Reason: it gains oxygen during the reaction *[1 mark]*.

 c) Iron oxide / Fe_2O_3 *[1 mark]*

Page 103 — Electrolysis

1 B *[1 mark]*

2 Anode: bromine *[1 mark]*
Cathode: lead *[1 mark]*

3 a) D *[1 mark]*

 b) Calcium is more reactive than hydrogen *[1 mark]*.

 c) chlorine *[1 mark]*

Page 104 — Electrolysis of Copper Sulfate

1 a)   E.g. a coating of copper/orange metal will form *[1 mark]*.
  b)   E.g. bubbles of (oxygen) gas will be produced *[1 mark]*.
2 a)   E.g. so she is only measuring the mass of the electrodes and not any of the solution *[1 mark]*.
  b) i)   Anode: the mass will decrease *[1 mark]*.
       Cathode: the mass will increase *[1 mark]*.
     ii)   Copper atoms in the anode turn into copper ions *[1 mark]* and move into the solution *[1 mark]*.

Page 105 — Tests for Gases

1 a)   damp blue litmus paper *[1 mark]*
  b)   chlorine *[1 mark]*
2 a)   E.g. the gas could be toxic/an irritant *[1 mark]*.
  b)   carbon dioxide *[1 mark]*
  c)   The gas was not hydrogen *[1 mark]*.
  d)   oxygen *[1 mark]*

Topic C4 — Predicting and Identifying Reactions and Products

Page 106 — Group 1 — Alkali Metals

Warm-up
low melting point, low boiling point and low density should be circled.

1 a)   1 *[1 mark]*
  b) Fr^+ *[1 mark]*
2 a)   sodium + water → **sodium hydroxide + hydrogen**
       [2 marks — 1 mark for each correct product.]
  b)   E.g. the sodium would float on the surface of the water *[1 mark]*, moving around and fizzing *[1 mark]*. The sodium would also melt/decrease in size *[1 mark]*.
  c)   The outer electron of potassium is further away from the nucleus than the outer electron of sodium *[1 mark]*. This means the outer electron of potassium is less attracted to the nucleus *[1 mark]* and more easily lost / less energy is needed to remove it *[1 mark]*.

Page 107 — Group 7 — Halogens

1   chlorine — green gas
    bromine — red-brown liquid
    iodine — dark grey solid
    [1 mark for all three correct.]
2   C *[1 mark]*
3 a) $2Li + Cl_2 →$ **$2LiCl$** *[1 mark for correct product, 1 mark for equation being correctly balanced.]*
  b)   The outer electron shell of chlorine is closer to the nucleus than the outer shell of iodine *[1 mark]*. This means it's easier for chlorine to gain an electron when it reacts *[1 mark]*.

Because of the increasing distance between the nucleus and the outer electron shell, reactivity decreases as you go down Group 7. Iodine is further down the group than chlorine, so its outer shell is further from the nucleus and it's less reactive than chlorine.

Page 108 — Halogen Displacement Reactions

1 a)   C *[1 mark]*
  b)   The sodium bromide and sodium iodide solutions both changed colour when the halogen was added *[1 mark]*. The halogen must be chlorine, since it can displace both bromine and iodine from halide solutions *[1 mark]*.
2 a)   iodine water/potassium bromide — no reaction
       bromine water/potassium chloride — no reaction
       bromine water/potassium iodide — reaction
       [3 marks — 1 mark for each correct answer.]
  b)   chlorine + potassium iodide → iodine + potassium chloride *[1 mark]*

Page 109 — Group 0 — Noble Gases

Warm-up
He, Ar, Xe and Ne should be circled.

1 a)   gas *[1 mark]*
  b)   B *[1 mark]*
  c)   They have a stable electron arrangement / full outer shell of electrons *[1 mark]*
2 a)   D *[1 mark]*
  b)   As you go down Group 0, the atoms of the elements increase in size *[1 mark]*. This means that there are greater forces of attraction between the atoms *[1 mark]*. More energy is needed to break these forces *[1 mark]*. So the boiling points of the elements increase as you go down the group *[1 mark]*.

Page 110 — Predicting Properties of Elements

1   D *[1 mark]*
2 a)   fluorine *[1 mark]*
If the boiling points of the elements increase as you go down a group, the one with the lowest boiling point must be at the top of the group.
  b)   solid *[1 mark]*
Since the melting points of the elements increase down Group 7, if the element above astatine is solid at room temperature and pressure, astatine should be solid too.
3   Any answer between 2 kg/m^3 and 5 kg/m^3 *[1 mark]*.

Page 111 — Reactivity of Metals

1 a)   Most reactive: magnesium
                         zinc
                         iron
       Least reactive: copper
       [1 mark for putting magnesium at the top and copper at the bottom. 1 mark for putting zinc above iron in the middle.]
  b) i)   Yes, because the more easily a metal forms positive ions the more reactive it is *[1 mark]* and metal Y is more reactive than metal Z *[1 mark]*.
     ii)   Metal X was sodium *[1 mark]*, because it reacted vigorously with cold water *[1 mark]*.

Page 112 — The Reactivity Series and Displacement

1 a)   Magnesium is more reactive than silver *[1 mark]* because magnesium can displace silver from its salt/compound / silver cannot displace magnesium from its salt/compound *[1 mark]*.
  b)   Tin is less reactive than zinc *[1 mark]* so cannot displace it from its salt/compound *[1 mark]*.
  c)   Iron and nickel *[1 mark]*, because they are both more reactive than tin / above tin in the reactivity series *[1 mark]*.

Topic C5 — Monitoring and Controlling Chemical Reactions

Page 113 — Reaction Rates

1 a)   The reading on the balance will fall *[1 mark]*.
  b)   E.g. a gas syringe *[1 mark]*.
Any sensible piece of equipment that you could use to measure the volume of gas produced or the change in mass of the mixture would be fine here.
2   E.g. mix the two solutions in a flask and place the flask on a piece of paper with a mark on it *[1 mark]*. Time how long it takes for the mark to be covered up by the precipitate *[1 mark]*. Repeat the experiment using different concentrations of the acid *[1 mark]*.
3   40 ÷ 125 = **0.32 cm^3/s**
    [1 mark for correct answer, 1 mark for correct units.]

Page 114 — Rate Experiments

1 a) Acid B, because it produced a greater volume of gas in the same period of time *[1 mark]*.

b) Dependent variable: volume of gas produced *[1 mark]*.
Independent variable: concentration of acid *[1 mark]*.

c) E.g.

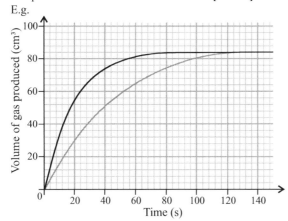

[1 mark for the new line starting off steeper than the original line, 1 mark for the new line levelling off at the same volume of gas produced as the original line.]

Page 115 — Calculating Rates

1 E.g.

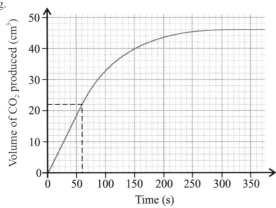

rate (gradient) = change in *y* ÷ change in *x*
= 22 ÷ 60 = 0.3666... = **0.37 cm³/s**

[2 marks for correct answer, otherwise 1 mark for dividing change in y by change in x.]

2 a) 40 °C: 1/t = 1 ÷ 41 = **0.024** s⁻¹
50 °C: 1/t = 1 ÷ 22 = **0.045** s⁻¹
60 °C: 1/t = 1 ÷ 10 = **0.100** s⁻¹
[1 mark for each correct answer]

b) At 30 °C the value of 1/t is twice as big as it is at 20 °C *[1 mark]*. So at 30 °C the reaction is going twice as fast as it is at 20 °C *[1 mark]*.

You also get the first mark here if you said anything that expressed the same idea. For example "At 20 °C the value of 1/t is 0.006, but at 30 °C the value of 1/t is 0.012", or even "0.012 ÷ 0.006 = 2".

Page 116 — Collision Theory

1 a) At the higher pressure there were more particles in the same volume *[1 mark]*. This increased the frequency of collisions between particles, which increased the rate *[1 mark]*.

b) E.g. temperature / absence of a catalyst *[1 mark]*

2 a) The rate of reaction would be faster at 35 °C than at 25 °C *[1 mark]*.

b) When the temperature is increased, particles move faster, so they collide more often *[1 mark]*. Increasing the temperature also increases the energy of the collisions *[1 mark]*. So the higher the temperature, the more successful collisions take place *[1 mark]* and the faster the rate of reaction gets *[1 mark]*.

c) It will be slower than the rate of Jonah's original reaction *[1 mark]*.

Page 117 — Collision Theory and Catalysts

Warm-up
You should have circled the reaction that uses the lump of calcium carbonate.

1 a) A — reactants *[1 mark]*
B — activation energy with catalyst *[1 mark]*
C — activation energy without catalyst *[1 mark]*
D — products *[1 mark]*

b) The catalyst decreases the activation energy needed for the reaction to occur *[1 mark]* by providing an alternative reaction pathway that has a lower energy *[1 mark]*.

Page 118 — Identifying Catalysts

1 a) C *[1 mark]*

b) E.g. the rate of reaction would fall to zero/greatly decrease *[1 mark]*.

2 a) 2, 4, 1, 5, 3 *[1 mark]*

b) Any two from: e.g. the reaction takes place at a higher rate/ produces a greater volume of gas in the same time / the mass of the copper oxide powder doesn't change / the appearance of the copper oxide powder doesn't change *[2 marks — 1 mark for each correct answer]*.

Page 119 — Dynamic Equilibrium

1 A *[1 mark]*

2 a) A reversible reaction is one where the products can react with each other to produce the original reactants *[1 mark]*.

b) temperature / pressure/concentration *[1 mark]*

3 a) C *[1 mark]*.

b) A closed system stops the reactants and products from escaping *[1 mark]*.

Topic C6 — Global Challenges

Page 120 — Extracting Metals from their Ores

1 a) calcium — electrolysis
copper — reduction with carbon
zinc — reduction with carbon
[3 marks — 1 mark for each correct answer]

b) lead *[1 mark]*

2 a) A rock which contains enough metal to make it worth extracting the metal from it *[1 mark]*.

b) Removing oxygen from a compound *[1 mark]*.

c) $2Fe_2O_3 + 3C \rightarrow 4Fe + 3CO_2$ *[1 mark]*

d) Magnesium is more reactive than carbon *[1 mark]*.

Page 121 — Extracting Metals with Electrolysis

1 a) E.g. because it uses a lots of electricity *[1 mark]*.

b) C *[1 mark]*

c) A — cathode
B — molten aluminium
C — anode
D — molten aluminium ore *[2 marks for all four correct, otherwise 1 mark for two correct]*

d) oxygen *[1 mark]*

Page 122 — Life-Cycle Assessments

Warm-up
Making the Material — Metal ore being mined and metal extracted from it.
Making the Product — Books being made from wood pulp.
Using the Product — A car using fuel while driving.
Product Disposal — Plastic bags going to landfill.

1 C *[1 mark]*.

2 a) E.g. mining metals can damage the environment / extracting/ processing metals uses lots of energy / extracting/processing metals causes pollution *[1 mark]*.

b) E.g. burning fossil fuels releases greenhouse gases/harmful substances / fossil fuels are finite resources so will eventually run out *[1 mark]*.

c) E.g. landfill sites take up space / landfill sites pollute land and water / transporting waste to landfill sites takes lots of energy / transporting waste to landfill sites can release pollutants *[2 marks — one mark for each correct answer]*.

Page 123 — Using Life-Cycle Assessments

1 Timber is made from a renewable source *[1 mark]*. Less energy is needed to produce the timber *[1 mark]*.

2 a) Toy C *[1 mark]*. Out of the three toys, producing toy C causes the lowest CO_2 emissions *[1 mark]* and uses the smallest amount of solvents *[1 mark]*. Producing toy C also uses much less energy than toy A, and only a little more than toy B *[1 mark]*.

b) E.g. whether the raw materials used to make the toys are sustainable / the amount of waste produced in making each toy / whether the toys are recyclable / whether any other toxic products are produced when the toys are made *[1 mark]*.

Any sensible environmental factor that the company might want to take into account when choosing which toy to produce gets a mark here.

Page 124 — Recycling Materials

1 B *[1 mark]*

2 a) Less energy is needed to recycle material B than A or C *[1 mark]*.

b) Any two from: e.g. Material A is abundant so conserving it through recycling is not as important. / Recycling material A uses a lot of energy. / Extracting material A does not use much energy *[2 marks — 1 mark for each correct reason]*.

c) E.g. the energy to extract Material C may come from burning fossil fuels, which could causes pollution/acid rain/climate change. / High energy processes use up lots of fossil fuels, and fossil fuels are a finite resource *[1 mark]*.

d) E.g. the paper will need to be separated from the plastic / it is difficult to separate the paper from the plastic *[1 mark]*.

Page 125 — Crude Oil

1 a) A *[1 mark]*
 b) E *[1 mark]*
 c) B *[1 mark]*
2 a) C_nH_{2n+2} *[1 mark]*
 b) dodecane *[1 mark]*

Page 126 — Hydrocarbons

Warm-up
Hydrocarbons are used to make plastics.
Hydrocarbons are used as fuel for transport.
Hydrocarbons are used to generate electricity.

1 D *[1 mark]*
2 a) A *[1 mark]*
 b) Long-chain hydrocarbons have stronger intermolecular forces between the chains than short-chain hydrocarbons *[1 mark]*. More energy is needed to overcome these forces and turn the hydrocarbons into a gas *[1 mark]*. So longer hydrocarbon molecules have higher boiling points *[1 mark]*.

Page 127 — Cracking

1 a) The amount of some fractions produced does not always meet the demand for those products *[1 mark]*. More of the product can be produced by cracking longer molecules into smaller, more useful ones *[1 mark]*.
 b) aluminium oxide *[1 mark]*
 c) A *[1 mark]*
2 B *[1 mark]*
The graph shows that diesel makes up 19% of the processed crude oil. So you need to work out what 19% of 500 tonnes would be.

Page 128 — The Atmosphere

1 a) C *[1 mark]*.
 b) Any two from: e.g. carbon dioxide / water vapour / named noble gas *[2 marks — 1 mark for each correct answer]*
 c) Green plants evolved *[1 mark]*, which produced oxygen during photosynthesis *[1 mark]*.
2 How to grade your answer:
  Level 0: There is no relevant information. *[No marks]*
  Level 1: There is a brief description of how carbon dioxide was originally released into the atmosphere and one point briefly describing how it was later removed. *[1 to 2 marks]*
  Level 2: There is some description of how carbon dioxide was originally released into the atmosphere and at least two points describing how it was later removed. *[3 to 4 marks]*
  Level 3: There is a good description of how carbon dioxide was originally released into the atmosphere and detailed points describing how it was later removed. *[5 to 6 marks]*
  Here are some points your answer may include:
  In the first billion years of Earth, carbon dioxide was released by erupting volcanoes that covered the Earth's surface.
  The early atmosphere contained mostly carbon dioxide.
  Over time, carbon dioxide was removed from the atmosphere.
  Much of the carbon dioxide dissolved in the oceans.
  Green plants also took in carbon dioxide through photosynthesis.
  Lots of carbon dioxide eventually got locked up in fossil fuels and rocks.
  There is now only a very small amount (0.04%) of carbon dioxide in the atmosphere.
  Carbon dioxide levels in the atmosphere are now increasing again due to humans burning fossil fuels and deforestation.

Pages 129-130 — The Greenhouse Effect and Global Warming

1 A *[1 mark]*
2 a) Less electricity will be used *[1 mark]*, so less fossil fuels will be burnt to produce electricity *[1 mark]*.
 b) E.g. walking/cycling instead of driving a car / turning central heating down / using electricity from renewable energy sources *[1 mark]*.
You'd get a mark here for describing any sensible way that a person could cut their carbon dioxide emissions.
3 a) The more fossil fuels humans burn, the higher the amount of carbon dioxide in Earth's atmosphere gets *[1 mark]*.
 b) Trees take carbon dioxide in during photosynthesis *[1 mark]*. Cutting trees down means there are fewer trees to take carbon dioxide out of the atmosphere *[1 mark]*.
 c) Global temperatures are likely to increase *[1 mark]*.
4 a) infrared radiation *[1 mark]*
 b) Some of the infrared radiation given out by the Earth is absorbed by greenhouse gases in the atmosphere *[1 mark]*. Some of it escapes into space *[1 mark]*.
5 a) The graph shows that the country's carbon dioxide emissions increased between 1960 and 2015 *[1 mark]*.
 b) E.g. the graph only shows the carbon dioxide emissions for one country, not for the whole world. / The graph does not show data about the amount of carbon dioxide in the atmosphere, only about the amount of carbon dioxide produced *[1 mark]*.
 c) E.g. flooding / changing rainfall patterns / extreme weather / melting polar ice caps *[1 mark]*.

Page 131 — Pollutants

1   Sulfur dioxide — Burning fossil fuels that contain sulfur impurities.
Nitrogen oxides — Reaction of gases in the air caused by the heat of burning fossil fuels.
Particulates — Incomplete combustion of hydrocarbons.
[2 marks, otherwise 1 mark for one correct answer]

2 a)   Sulfur dioxide / nitrogen oxides/nitrogen monoxide/nitrogen dioxide *[1 mark]*

   b)   Any two from: e.g. it can kill plants/animals / damage buildings / damage statues / corrode metals *[2 marks — 1 mark for each correct answer]*.

3 a)   E.g. carbon monoxide stops blood from carrying oxygen around the body *[1 mark]*. The lack of oxygen can cause fainting, a coma or death *[1 mark]*.

   b)   E.g. particulates can cause or worsen breathing problems / create a coating of soot on buildings *[1 mark]*.

   c)   E.g. there are more cars in cities than in the country *[1 mark]*.

Page 132 — Water Treatment

1 a)   D *[1 mark]*

   b)   E.g. fresh water supplies are limited because they depend on rainfall *[1 mark]*.

2 a)   Any two from, e.g. rivers / lakes / reservoirs *[2 marks — 1 mark for each correct answer]*

   b)   E.g. processing fresh water takes less energy than desalination *[1 mark]* which makes it less expensive *[1 mark]*.

   c)   How to grade your answer:

Level 0:   There is no relevant information. *[No marks]*

Level 1:   The answer gives a very brief description of how surface water is treated to give drinking water. Some of the steps may be missing and there is little explanation of the purposes of the steps given. *[1 to 2 marks]*

Level 2:   The answer gives a good description of how surface water is treated to give drinking water. All three main steps are mentioned and some attempt has been made to explain the purpose of each step. *[3 to 4 marks]*

Level 3:   The answer gives a full and clear description of how surface water is treated to give drinking water. All three main steps are fully described and a clear explanation is given of the purpose of each step. *[5 to 6 marks]*

Here are some points your answer may include:
The first step in treating the water is filtration.
The water is filtered through a wire mesh and then through gravel/sand beds.
Filtration removes large solid objects/bits from the water.
The second step in treating the water is sedimentation.
During this step, chemicals are added to make any fine solid particles that are left in the water clump together.
The clumps settle at the bottom and can then be removed.
The third step in treating the water is chlorination.
Chlorine gas is bubbled through the water.
The chlorine gas kills harmful bacteria and other microbes.

Topic P1 — Matter

Page 133 — The History of the Atom and Atomic Structure

Warm-up
1×10^{-10} m

1   C *[1 mark]*

2 a)   Most of the atom is empty space *[1 mark]*.

   b)   Some particles were deflected/bounced back *[1 mark]*.

   c)   There is a nucleus at the centre of the atom *[1 mark]*. This is surrounded by electrons in fixed shells *[1 mark]*.

Page 134 — Density

1 a)   volume = 0.016 × 1.25 *[1 mark]*
     = **0.020 m³** *[1 mark]*

   b)   density = mass ÷ volume
So, density = 90.0 ÷ 0.020 *[1 mark]*
     = **4500 kg/m³** *[1 mark]*

2 a)   Place the empty beaker on the mass balance and zero it *[1 mark]*. Pour some oil into the beaker and record the volume *[1 mark]* and the mass of the oil *[1 mark]*. The density can then be found using density = mass ÷ volume *[1 mark]*.

   b)   A *[1 mark]*

Page 135 — Particle Theory and States of Matter

Warm-up

Solid   Liquid   Gas

1 a)   C *[1 mark]*

   b) i)   sublimation *[1 mark]*

     ii)   E.g. the change of state can be reversed *[1 mark]*.

2 a)   B *[1 mark]*

   b)   stay the same *[1 mark]*

Page 136 — Specific Heat Capacity

1   The temperature of the substance increases *[1 mark]*.
The substance changes state *[1 mark]*.

2 a)   It is the energy needed to raise the temperature of 1 kg of that substance by 1 °C *[1 mark]*.

   b)   The amount of energy used to heat the aluminium *[1 mark]*.

   c)   E.g. to identify anomalies / check for repeatability / to find consistent values and calculate a mean *[1 mark]*.

   d)   specific heat capacity = change in thermal energy ÷ (mass × change in temperature)
mass (in kg) = mass (in g) ÷ 1000
     = 250 ÷ 1000 = 0.25 kg *[1 mark]*
So, specific heat capacity = 9100 ÷ (0.25 × 52) *[1 mark]*
     = **700 J/kg °C** *[1 mark]*

Page 137 — Specific Latent Heat

1 a)   Between 3 and 8 minutes: <u>Substance is melting</u> *[1 mark]*
Between 24 and 35 minutes: <u>Substance is boiling</u> *[1 mark]*

   b)   thermal energy for a change in state = mass × specific latent heat so, specific latent heat = thermal energy for a change in state ÷ mass *[1 mark]*
specific latent heat = 34 000 ÷ 0.50 *[1 mark]*
     = **68 000 J/kg** *[1 mark]*

Page 138 — Motion of Gas Particles

1   C *[1 mark]*

2 a)   The gas particles in the tyre collide with the tyre wall *[1 mark]*. Each time a gas particle hits the tyre wall, it exerts a force *[1 mark]*. The overall force caused by all the collisions in a given area is the pressure *[1 mark]*.

   b)   The particles would collide with the tyre walls more often *[1 mark]*. This would mean the pressure would increase *[1 mark]*.

c)　On a hot day, the air particles in the tyre would have more energy in their kinetic energy stores *[1 mark]*, so they would move faster *[1 mark]*. This means they would hit the tyre walls harder and more often, creating more pressure *[1 mark]*.

Topic P2 — Forces

Page 139 — Speed and Velocity

Warm-up

Scalar	Vector
speed	velocity
distance	displacement

1 a)　distance travelled = speed × time
$$= 1.5 \times 120 \text{ [1 mark]}$$
$$= \textbf{180} \text{ [1 mark]}$$
Unit = **m** *[1 mark]*

　 b)　distance travelled = speed × time
So, speed = distance travelled ÷ time *[1 mark]*
$$= 5100 \div 2040 \text{ [1 mark]}$$
$$= \textbf{2.5 m/s} \text{ [1 mark]}$$

2 a)　2.0 hours in seconds: $2.0 \times (60 \times 60) = 7200$ s *[1 mark]*
(average) speed = distance ÷ time
$$= 180\,000 \div 7200 \text{ [1 mark]}$$
$$= \textbf{25 m/s} \text{ [1 mark]}$$

　 b)　Speed is a scalar quantity, and so only has a magnitude / a size, which hasn't changed *[1 mark]*. Velocity is a vector quantity, so it has a direction too. Since direction has changed, the velocity must also have changed *[1 mark]*.

Page 140 — Measurements of Motion

Warm-up

Equipment	Quantity Measured	
	Distance	Time
Metre stick	✓	
Stopwatch		✓
Light gate connected to a computer		✓

1 a)　$230 \times 1000 = 230\,000$ m *[1 mark]*

　 b)　72 km/hr in m/hr: $72 \times 1000 = 72\,000$ m/hr *[1 mark]*
72 000 m/hr in m/s: $72\,000 \div (60 \times 60)$
$$= \textbf{20 m/s} \text{ [1 mark]}$$

2　The student should use a trundle wheel *[1 mark]*.
The football field is many metres long, so a trundle wheel is more appropriate *[1 mark]*.

Page 141 — Acceleration

1　B *[1 mark]*

2　(final velocity)² – (initial velocity)² = 2 × acceleration × distance
So, acceleration = ((final velocity)² – (initial velocity)²) ÷ (2 × distance) *[1 mark]*
$$= (32^2 - 18^2) \div (2 \times 350) \text{ [1 mark]}$$
$$= \textbf{1.0 m/s}^2 \text{ [1 mark]}$$

3 a)　B *[1 mark]*
acceleration = change in velocity ÷ time = (3.2 – 0) ÷ 8.0 = 0.4 m/s²

　 b)　total time travelling = $8.0 + 7.0 = 15.0$ s
change in velocity = acceleration × time *[1 mark]*
$$= 0.4 \times 15.0 \text{ [1 mark]}$$
$$= \textbf{6 m/s} \text{ [1 mark]}$$

Even if you got a) wrong, you'd get the marks for b) if you used the correct method.

Page 142 — Investigating Motion

1 a)　How to grade your answer:
Level 0:　There is no relevant information. *[No marks]*
Level 1:　There are only a couple of relevant points about the experiment, with no description of how to calculate the acceleration. *[1 to 2 marks]*
Level 2:　There is a brief explanation of how the experiment is carried out, and how to calculate the acceleration. *[3 to 4 marks]*
Level 3:　There is a detailed explanation of how the experiment is carried out, including details on how to calculate the acceleration from the results. *[5 to 6 marks]*

Here are some points your answer may include:
Alice should release the trolley from rest at marker A.
She should use the stopwatch to measure the time taken for the trolley to reach marker B and marker C after its release.
As the trolley started from rest its initial speed was zero.
The final speed can be found by dividing the distance between B and C by the time taken to pass from B to C.
The acceleration can be found using: acceleration = change in velocity ÷ time (ignoring friction).
The change in speed is equal to the final speed.
The time is the time taken for the trolley to travel from A to B.

　 b)　Light gates are generally more accurate than using a stopwatch / they eliminate human error / speed and acceleration can be calculated for you *[1 mark]*

　 c)　It would increase *[1 mark]*.
A greater angle will give a greater acceleration on the ramp, which will give a greater speed on the runway.

Page 143 — Distance-Time Graphs

1　A *[1 mark]*

2 a)　360 m *[1 mark]*

　 b)　120 s *[1 mark]*

　 c)　Average speed = gradient = change in the vertical ÷ change in the horizontal *[1 mark]* $= (500 - 0) \div (430 - 0)$ *[1 mark]*
$= 1.162... = \textbf{1.2}$ to two significant figures *[1 mark]*

Pages 144 — Velocity-Time Graphs

1　B *[1 mark]*

2 a)　D *[1 mark]*
E.g.

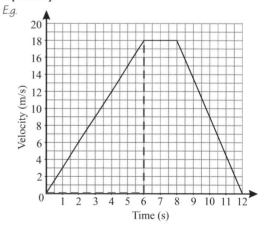

acceleration = gradient = change in the vertical ÷ change in the horizontal = (18 – 0) ÷ (6 – 0) = 3.0 m/s²

　 b)　6 s and 8 s *[1 mark]*

Page 145 — Forces and Free Body Force Diagrams

1 a) A resultant force is a single force *[1 mark]* that has the same effect as all the individual forces acting on an object *[1 mark]*.

b) Magnitude = 10 000 N *[1 mark]* Direction = Right *[1 mark]*

The forces acting up and down are equal and act in opposite directions, so cancel each other out. The forces acting left and right combine to give a resultant force of 20 000 − 10 000 = 10 000 N to the right.

2 Contact force: friction / tension / normal contact force *[1 mark]*

Non-contact force: weight / gravitational force *[1 mark]*

3 a) A: Normal contact force *[1 mark]*

B: Weight *[1 mark]*

b)

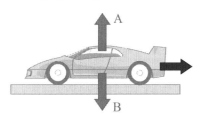

[1 mark for an arrow pointing towards the right]

Pages 146-147 — Newton's Laws of Motion

Warm-up

Newton's First Law of motion says that an object will remain stationary or continue moving at a constant velocity if there is a <u>zero</u> resultant force acting on it. If there is a <u>non-zero</u> resultant force acting on it, it will accelerate.

1 C *[1 mark]*

2 force = mass × acceleration,

So, acceleration = force ÷ mass *[1 mark]*

= 2400 ÷ 400 *[1 mark]*

= **6 m/s²** *[1 mark]*

3 a) 320 N *[1 mark]*

b) 640 N *[1 mark]*

4 a) B *[1 mark]*

As F = ma = 550 000 × 5.0 = 2 750 000 N.

b) There are no forces from the thrusters or from air resistance/friction *[1 mark]*. Therefore the resultant force acting on the rocket is zero *[1 mark]*. Newton's First Law states that an object will continue travelling at a constant velocity if the resultant force on it is zero *[1 mark]*.

Page 148 — Mass, Weight and Gravity

Warm-up

'A given object will have the same weight anywhere in the universe' is false.

Weight changes depending on the strength of the gravitational field the object is located in.

1 a) Weight is the force due to gravity/acting on an object when it's in a gravitational field *[1 mark]*.

b) weight = mass × gravitational field strength

= 60 × 10 *[1 mark]*

= **600 N** *[1 mark]*

2 a) weight = mass × gravitational field strength

So, mass = weight ÷ gravitational field strength *[1 mark]*

= 2000 ÷ 10 *[1 mark]*

= **200 kg** *[1 mark]*

b) weight = mass × gravitational field strength

So, gravitational field strength = weight ÷ mass *[1 mark]*

= 700 ÷ 200 *[1 mark]*

= 3.5 N/kg

= **4 N/kg** (to 1 s.f.) *[1 mark]*

Page 149 — Mechanical Energy Stores

1 D *[1 mark]*

potential energy = mass × height × gravitational field strength

= 70 × 10 × 10 = 7000 J

2 a) potential energy = mass × height × gravitational field strength

So, height = potential energy ÷ (mass × gravitational field strength) *[1 mark]*

= 16 ÷ (0.50 × 10) *[1 mark]*

= **3.2 m** *[1 mark]*

b) kinetic energy = ½ × mass × (speed)²

2 × kinetic energy = mass × (speed)²

(2 × kinetic energy) ÷ mass = (speed)²

speed = $\sqrt{(2 \times \text{kinetic energy}) \div \text{mass}}$ *[1 mark]*

= $\sqrt{(2 \times 16) \div 0.50}$ *[1 mark]*

= **8.0 m/s** *[1 mark]*

Pages 150 — Work Done

1 a) D *[1 mark]*

One newton-metre of work is equal to 150 J of energy transferred.

b) Any two from: E.g. kinetic energy store / gravitational potential energy store / thermal energy store *[1 mark]*

2 a) 150 cm in metres: 150 ÷ 100 = 1.5 m *[1 mark]*

work done = force × distance = 60 × 1.5 *[1 mark]*

= **90 J** *[1 mark]*

b) weight / gravity force *[1 mark]*

3 a) work done = force × distance

So, force = work done ÷ distance *[1 mark]*

= 750 ÷ 15 = **50 N** *[1 mark]*

b) The temperature of the wheels increases *[1 mark]*. This is because doing work against frictional forces causes energy to be transferred to the thermal energy stores of the wheels *[1 mark]*.

Page 151 — Power

Warm-up

Power is the <u>rate of</u> energy transfer or <u>work done</u>.

It is measured in <u>watts</u>.

1 a) A *[1 mark]*

b) Bulb Y *[1 mark]*. Bulb Y transfers more energy than Bulb X in the same amount of time. Power = energy ÷ time so Bulb Y has the highest power *[1 mark]*.

2 Power = $\dfrac{\text{energy transferred}}{\text{time}}$

So, time = $\dfrac{\text{energy transferred}}{\text{power}}$ *[1 mark]*

= $\dfrac{16\,800}{35}$ *[1 mark]* = **480 s** *[1 mark]*

Page 152 — Forces and Elasticity

1 a) One force would just make the spring move not change shape *[1 mark]*.

b) elastic deformation *[1 mark]*

c) plastic deformation *[1 mark]*

2 force = spring constant × extension

So, spring constant = force ÷ extension *[1 mark]*

= 240 ÷ 0.20 *[1 mark]*

= **1200** *[1 mark]*

Unit = **N/m** *[1 mark]*

Page 153 — Forces, Elasticity and Work Done

Warm-up

When an object obeys Hooke's Law the relationship between the force applied and its extension is <u>linear</u>. This means that the amount an object extends is <u>directly proportional to</u> the amount of force applied.

1 A *[1 mark]*

2 extension = 0.087 − 0.072 = 0.015 m

energy transferred = 0.5 × spring constant × (extension)²

= 0.5 × 24 × 0.015² *[1 mark]*

= **0.0027** *[1 mark]*

Unit = **Nm or J** *[1 mark]*

Page 154 — Using Force Extension Graphs

1 a)

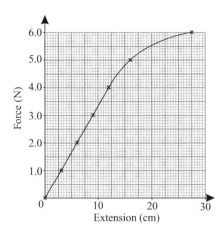

[1 mark for both points plotted correctly, 1 mark for line of best fit being straight between 0-4 N, 1 mark for curved line between 4-6 N]

b) 3.3 N *[1 mark]*

Accept answers from 3.2–3.4 N.

c) area under the graph between 0 and 6.0 cm extension:
area of a triangle = 0.5 × base × height
base = 6.0 cm = 0.060 m *[1 mark]*
height = 2.0 N
So, area of a triangle = 0.5 × 0.06 × 2.0 *[1 mark]*
= **0.06 J** *[1 mark]*

You would also get the marks if you counted the number of squares under the graph and used it to work out the area.

Page 155 — Investigating Hooke's Law

1 a) Firstly, measure the original (natural) length of the spring *[1 mark]*. Then find the weight of one of the masses *[1 mark]*. Add the masses one at a time to the spring and measure the new extension of the spring each time *[1 mark]*. Plot a graph of the weight of the masses against extension and find the gradient of the linear part of the graph. This gives the spring constant *[1 mark]*.

b) Spring constant = force ÷ extension = gradient when linear
= change in vertical ÷ change in horizontal
= 4 ÷ 8 *[1 mark]*
= **0.5 N/cm** *[1 mark]*

c) E.g. if the masses fall, she can get out of the way easily *[1 mark]*

Topic P3 — Electricity and Magnetism

Page 156 — Static Electricity

1 a) B *[1 mark]*

b) Neutral matter contains an equal number of positive and negative charges *[1 mark]*, so their effects cancel each other out/it has zero net charge *[1 mark]*.

2 a) When the rods are rubbed with the cloth, electrons are transferred from the rods to the cloth *[1 mark]*.

b) Both rods have a positive charge *[1 mark]*. This means they repel each other and the hanging rod moves away *[1 mark]*.

c) When the positive rod is held near the paper scraps, electrons are attracted towards the surface of the paper, and so a charge is induced in the paper *[1 mark]*, giving the surface a negative charge *[1 mark]*. Opposite charges attract, so the paper is attracted to the rod and 'jumps' towards it *[1 mark]*.

Page 157 — Current and Circuit Diagrams

Warm-up

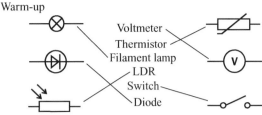

1 a) A battery/cell *[1 mark]*. The battery/cell acts as source of potential difference so that charge can flow *[1 mark]*.

b) D *[1 mark]*.

2 a) C *[1 mark]*

charge = current × time = 3.5 × 120 = 420 C

b) charge = current × time
so, time = charge ÷ current *[1 mark]* = 770 ÷ 3.5 *[1 mark]*
= **220 s** *[1 mark]*

Page 158 — Potential Difference

1 potential difference = current × resistance
= 3.0 × 6.0 *[1 mark]* = **18 V** *[1 mark]*

2 a) D *[1 mark]*

resistance = potential difference ÷ current = 6.0 ÷ 4.0 = 1.5 Ω

b) energy transferred = charge × potential difference
= 40 × 6.0 *[1 mark]* = **240 J** *[1 mark]*

c) The potential difference across a component is the amount of energy transferred (to that component) *[1 mark]* per unit charge passed *[1 mark]*.

Page 159 — I-V Characteristics

1 a) B *[1 mark]*

B is a straight line, so it must be of a linear circuit element.

b) Read the current off the graph and divide the potential difference by it ($R = V \div I$) *[1 mark]*.

2 a) E.g. set the resistance of the variable resistor *[1 mark]*. Take readings of the current through and the potential difference across the component *[1 mark]*. Then change the resistance of the variable resistor and take readings of current and potential difference. Repeat this for a range of values *[1 mark]*.

b) Read potential difference, when current is 2.0 A, off the graph
potential difference = 6 V *[1 mark]*
potential difference = current × resistance
so, resistance = potential difference ÷ current *[1 mark]*
= 6 ÷ 2.0 *[1 mark]*
= **3 Ω** *[1 mark]*

Page 160 — Circuit Devices

1 B *[1 mark]*

2 a) Because there is a very high resistance in one direction *[1 mark]*.

b) increases *[1 mark]*

3 a) D *[1 mark]*.

b) B *[1 mark]*. For any potential difference, the current through B is smaller. As $V = I \times R$, the resistance of B must be higher *[1 mark]*.

Page 161 — Series Circuits

1 A *[1 mark]*

2 C *[1 mark]*

3 a) D *[1 mark]*

b) 0.05 A *[1 mark]*

The circuit is the same everywhere in a series circuit ($I_1 = I_2 = I_3$).

Page 162 — Series and Parallel Circuits

Warm-up
B
1 a)   D *[1 mark]*
The total current in the circuit is split between the two branches, so the current through the ammeter is found by adding the current through R_1 and R_2.
  b)   C *[1 mark]*
The total potential difference across each branch of a parallel circuit is the same as the source potential difference.
  c)   B *[1 mark]*

Page 163 — Energy and Power in Circuits

1 a)   150 J are transferred every second *[1 mark]*.
  b)   power = potential difference × current
       so, current = power ÷ potential difference *[1 mark]*
          = 150 ÷ 60.0 *[1 mark]* = **2.5 A** *[1 mark]*
  c)   Convert 150 W into kW: 150 ÷ 1000 = 0.15 kW *[1 mark]*
       Energy transferred = power × time = 0.15 × 2 *[1 mark]*
       = **0.3 kWh** *[1 mark]*
2 a)   energy transferred = power × time
       so, time = energy transferred ÷ power *[1 mark]*
       = 180 000 ÷ 900 *[1 mark]* = **200 s** *[1 mark]*
  b)   power = (current)² × resistance
       so, current = $\sqrt{\dfrac{\text{power}}{\text{resistance}}}$ *[1 mark]*
       = $\sqrt{\dfrac{900}{14}}$ = 8.017.... *[1 mark]* = **8 A** *[1 mark]*

Page 164 — Magnets and Magnetic Fields

Warm-up
From left to right: attractive, repulsive
1   C *[1 mark]*
2   B *[1 mark]*
3   The Earth has a magnetic field / The Earth's core is magnetic *[1 mark]*. The needle in the compass is magnetic and is attracted to the Earth's magnetic north pole *[1 mark]*.

Page 165 — Electromagnetism

1 a)

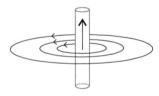

[1 mark for the arrows pointing in the correct direction (anti-clockwise)]
  b)   D *[1 mark]*
  c)   It increases *[1 mark]*.
2 a)   X *[1 mark]*
  b)   It will decrease *[1 mark]*. A smaller current means a weaker magnetic field *[1 mark]*.

Topic P4 — Waves and Radioactivity

Page 166 — Wave Basics

Warm-up
sound waves — **L**
ripples on water — **T**
1 a)   B *[1 mark]*
  b)   D *[1 mark]*
  c)   The vibrations in longitudinal waves are in the same direction as the direction of energy transfer *[1 mark]*. In transverse waves, the vibrations are perpendicular (at right angles) to the direction of energy transfer *[1 mark]*.
2   She's incorrect *[1 mark]*. It is the wave, not the water, that moves (so the leaf will just move up and down) *[1 mark]*.

Page 167 — Wave Speed

1 a)   D *[1 mark]*
  b)   wave speed = frequency × wavelength *[1 mark]*
       = 50.0 × 6.80 *[1 mark]*
       = **340 m/s** *[1 mark]*

Page 168 — Measuring Waves

1 a)   Any two from: e.g. the speed of the motor / the position of the dipper / the position of the cork when she starts timing / the depth of water in the tank / the equipment used *[1 mark for each correct answer]*.
  b)   (35 + 37 + 36) ÷ 3 = **36** *[1 mark]*
  c)   36 ÷ 30 = **1.2 Hz** *[1 mark]*
You'd still get the mark here if your answer to part b) was wrong but you'd used the correct method.
  d)   60 ÷ 3 = **20 cm** *[1 mark]*

Page 169 — Reflection

1 a)   B *[1 mark]*
  b)   50° *[1 mark]*
Remember — angle of incidence = angle of reflection.
2   E.g. Trace the path that the light takes *[1 mark]*. Measure the angle of incidence (between incident ray and normal) and the angle of reflection (between the reflected ray and the normal) *[1 mark]*.

Page 170 — Refraction

1 a)   E.g. when a wave changes direction as it crosses a boundary *[1 mark]*.
  b)   The wave is travelling along the normal / at right angles to the boundary *[1 mark]*.
2   E.g.

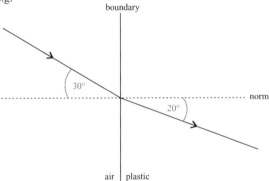

[1 mark for an incident ray drawn on the left of the boundary and a refracted ray drawn on the right of the boundary with correct arrows on both rays, 1 mark for correctly drawn normal, 1 mark for incident ray at 30° to the normal (on either side of the normal), 1 mark for refracted ray at 20° to the normal on the opposite side of the normal to the incident ray]
You don't need to have labelled the angles in your diagram, we've just included them here to make it clearer.
3   It will be larger than 20° *[1 mark]*. E.g. when light travelled from air to water, the light ray bent towards the normal/the angle of refraction was smaller than the angle of incidence. This means that for a light ray travelling from water to air, the ray will bend away from the normal/the angle of refraction will be larger than the angle of incidence *[1 mark]*. / As the light ray will be travelling from a denser to a less dense material, it must bend away from the normal *[1 mark]*.

Page 171 — Investigating Refraction

1 a) E.g. a ray box creates a thin beam of light which lets you make more accurate measurements of angles *[1 mark]*.

b)

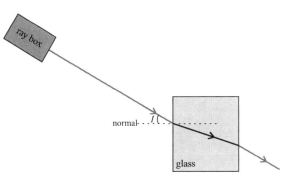

[1 mark for correctly completed diagram]

c) 30° (Allow any answer between 29° and 31°) *[1 mark]*

d) Any two from: e.g. use the same glass block / make sure the pencil is always sharp / use the same protractor / use the same ray box *[1 mark for each correct answer]*.

Page 172 — Electromagnetic Waves

1 a) gamma rays *[1 mark]*
b) radio waves *[1 mark]*
2 B *[1 mark]*
3 Ionising radiation can be absorbed by the skin *[1 mark]* which may lead to tissue damage and/or cancer *[1 mark]*.
4 Electromagnetic waves travel at the same speed through space *[1 mark]*. Since wave speed = frequency × wavelength, if the frequency of the wave increases, the wavelength must decrease *[1 mark]*. So the wavelength of the high frequency electromagnetic wave must be smaller than that of the low frequency wave *[1 mark]*.

Page 173 — Uses of EM Waves

Warm-up
Communications and TV should be circled.

1 C *[1 mark]*
2 a) A *[1 mark]*
b) E.g. heating / cooking food *[1 mark]*
3 Microwaves given out by the oven are absorbed by water in the food *[1 mark]*. Energy from the microwaves is transferred to the water, causing it to heat up *[1 mark]*. This causes the rest of the food to heat up and cook *[1 mark]*.

Page 174 — More Uses of EM Waves

1 a) A *[1 mark]*
b) i) C *[1 mark]*
ii) E.g. suntanning / security marking *[1 mark]*
2 a) X-rays *[1 mark]*, gamma rays *[1 mark]*
b) E.g. in medical imaging / in medical tracers / to sterilise equipment *[1 mark]*.

Page 175 — Atoms and Isotopes

1 a) D *[1 mark]*
b) +56 *[1 mark]*
2 a) Atoms with the same number of protons but a different number of neutrons *[1 mark]*.
b) Mass number = 23 *[1 mark]*
Number of neutrons = 23 − 11 = **12** *[1 mark]*
c) D *[1 mark]*

Page 176 — Electron Energy Levels

Warm-up

The cross can be anywhere on the outer shell (outer circle).

1 Positively-charged *[1 mark]*. There are now more positively-charged protons than negatively-charged electrons *[1 mark]*.
2 A *[1 mark]*

Page 177 — Radioactive Decay

1 B *[1 mark]*
2 The relative mass of an alpha particle is 4 *[1 mark]*. Gamma radiation has no charge *[1 mark]*.
3 Gamma *[1 mark]*, because the radiation passes through the aluminium *[1 mark]*.

Page 178 — Decay Equations

Warm-up
$^{0}_{0}\gamma$

1 a) Mass number: Doesn't change *[1 mark]*.
Atomic number: Increases by 1 *[1 mark]*.
b) It increases by 1 *[1 mark]*.
2 a) α / He^{2+} / alpha particle *[1 mark]*
b) $a = 211 − 4 = 207$ *[1 mark]*
$b = 87 − 2 = 85$ *[1 mark]*
c) $^{207}_{85}\text{At} \rightarrow {}^{203}_{83}\text{Bi} + {}^{4}_{2}\alpha$ *[1 mark for correct mass numbers, 1 mark for correct atomic numbers and 1 mark for alpha or helium (He) symbol]*

Page 179 — Activity and Half-Life

1 The half-life is the average time taken for the activity/count rate of a source to halve *[1 mark]*.

2 a)

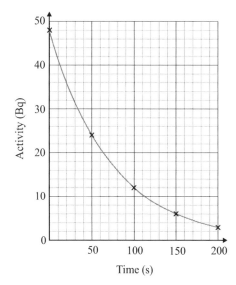

[1 mark for both points correctly plotted, 1 mark for a smooth single curve passing through all points]

b) 9 Bq (accept between 8 and 10) *[1 mark]*

Page 180 — Dangers of Radioactivity

1 a) There is no contamination risk *[1 mark]* as the source isn't touching the object and can't flow to it as it is a solid *[1 mark]*.
b) The type of radiation emitted by the source *[1 mark]* and the object's distance from the source *[1 mark]*.
2 C *[1 mark]*

3   Gases can flow and come into contact with people *[1 mark]*. They can also be easily breathed in, contaminating people from the inside *[1 mark]*.

Topic P5 — Energy

Page 181 — Energy and Energy Transfers
Warm-up
Circled: elastic potential, nuclear, thermal.
1   B *[1 mark]*
2   D *[1 mark]*
3 a)   chemical *[1 mark]*
  b)   electrically *[1 mark]*
  c)   Energy can be transferred usefully, stored or dissipated *[1 mark]*, but can never be created or destroyed *[1 mark]*.
  d)   E.g. thermal energy store (of the wire/bulb filament) *[1 mark]*

Page 182 — More Energy Transfers
1   A car slowing down without braking. — kinetic energy store
     A mug of hot tea cooling down. — thermal energy store
     A stretched rubber band returning to its original shape. — elastic potential energy store
     An acorn falling from a tree. — gravitational potential energy store
     [3 marks for all four correct, otherwise 2 marks for two correct and 1 mark for one correct]
2 a)   Energy is not transferred by heating to the water's chemical store. It is transferred by heating to the water's thermal energy store *[1 mark]*.
     This does not cause the water temperature to decrease. It causes it to increase *[1 mark]*.
  b)   The oil has a different specific heat capacity to the water *[1 mark]*. So the same amount of transferred energy will increase the temperature of the oil by a different amount compared to water *[1 mark]*.
3   Energy is transferred mechanically *[1 mark]* from the bicycle's kinetic energy store *[1 mark]* to the thermal energy store of the brake pads *[1 mark]*.

Page 183 — Efficiency
1 a)   D *[1 mark]*
  b)   wasted energy = input energy – useful energy output
                  = 50 – 40 *[1 mark]*
                  = **10 J** *[1 mark]*
2   efficiency (percentage) = (useful output energy transfer ÷ input energy transfer) × 100 *[1 mark]*
                  = (16 000 ÷ 20 000) × 100 *[1 mark]*
                  = **80%** *[1 mark]*
3   Convert 60% to a decimal: 60 ÷ 100 = 0.60
     efficiency (as a decimal) = useful output energy transfer ÷ input energy transfer
     So, input energy transfer = useful output energy transfer ÷ efficiency (as a decimal) *[1 mark]*
                  = 1200 ÷ 0.60 *[1 mark]*
                  = **2000 J** *[1 mark]*

Page 184 — Reducing Unwanted Energy Transfers
Warm-up
Circled: Add roof insulation, Use walling material with a low thermal conductivity.
1   C *[1 mark]*
2   The oil will act as a lubricant, reducing friction between the moving parts of the bike chain *[1 mark]*. This will reduce the amount of energy dissipated *[1 mark]*.
3   D *[1 mark]*. Rate of cooling goes down with brick thickness, so thicker bricks will have a slower rate of cooling *[1 mark]*. Rate of cooling is also proportional to thermal conductivity, so bricks with lower thermal conductivity will have a slower rate of cooling *[1 mark]*.

Page 185 — Mechanical Energy Transfers & Calculations
1   B *[1 mark]*
2   B *[1 mark]*
Use the equation:
Energy transferred in stretching = 0.5 × spring constant × (extension)²
3 a)   kinetic energy = 0.5 × mass × (speed)²
                  = 0.5 × 60 × 10² *[1 mark]*
                  = **3000 J** *[1 mark]*
  b)   potential energy = mass × height × gravitational field strength *[1 mark]*
     So, height = potential energy ÷ (mass × gravitational field strength) *[1 mark]*
                  = 3000 ÷ (60 × 10) *[1 mark]*
                  = **5 m** *[1 mark]*
If you got a different answer in question 3a, you would still get the marks here if you used your answer and the correct method.

Page 186 — Electrical Energy Transfers & Calculations
1   B *[1 mark]*
2   B and C *[1 mark]*
     power = potential difference × current
     B: 6 × 0.3 = 1.8 W
     C: 3 × 0.6 = 1.8 W *[1 mark]*
Also, A: 9 × 1.5 = 13.5 W and D: 6 × 1.5 = 9 W
3 a)   B *[1 mark]*
  b)   3.0 kW = 3.0 × 1000 W = 3000 W *[1 mark]*
     energy transferred = power × time
                  = 3000 × 120 *[1 mark]*
                  = **360 000** *[1 mark]* **J** *[1 mark]*

Topic P6 — Global Challenges

Page 187 — Everyday Speeds and Accelerations
1   B *[1 mark]*
2   The airbag slows the passenger down over a longer period of time, reducing their deceleration *[1 mark]*. This reduces the forces on the passenger (since $F = ma$) *[1 mark]*. There is a lower risk of injury if the forces involved are smaller *[1 mark]*.
3 a)   90.0 × 1.6 = **144 km/h** *[1 mark]*
  b)   144 × 1000 ÷ 60 ÷ 60 = **40 m/s** *[1 mark]*
You could also convert from km/hr to m/s by dividing by 3.6.
4   E.g. assuming it takes cyclist 7.0 s to accelerate.
     acceleration = change in velocity ÷ time
                  = 5.5 ÷ 7.0 = 0.7857...
                  = **0.79 m/s²** (to 2 s.f.)
     [1 mark for estimated acceleration time between 4 and 11 seconds, 1 mark for substituting values into the equation and 1 mark for an answer matching the calculation given to 2 s.f.]

Page 188 — Stopping Distances and Reaction Times
1 a)   B *[1 mark]*
  b)   Driver's thinking distance = 22 – 14
                  = **8 m** *[1 mark]*
To answer this question, you need to know that:
stopping distance = thinking distance + braking distance.
So, thinking distance = stopping distance − braking distance.
2 a)   (0.69 + 0.42 + 0.51) ÷ 3 *[1 mark]* = **0.54 s** *[1 mark]*
  b)   E.g. Kate is more tired in the evening *[1 mark]*.

Page 189 — Non-Renewable Energy Sources
Warm-up
Coal and uranium should be circled.
1   C *[1 mark]*
2 a)   B *[1 mark]*
  b) i)   E.g. global warming / climate change *[1 mark]*
     ii)   E.g. acid rain / the possibility of oil spills *[1 mark]*

Page 190 — Renewable Energy Sources
1 a) B *[1 mark]*
  b) D *[1 mark]*
2 E.g. The average wind speed between October and March was higher than between April and September, so wind turbines will be able to generate more electricity between October and March than between April and September *[1 mark]*. Between April and September, the average number of daylight hours was higher than between October and March, so solar panels will be able to generate more electricity between April and September than between October and March *[1 mark]*. So when one of the methods of generating electricity is producing less, the other method will be producing more *[1 mark]*. By installing both, the business will have a more reliable electricity supply throughout the year *[1 mark]*.

Page 191 — More on Energy Sources
Warm-up
H
1 a) 1995: 56 + 10 + 16 = **82%**
  2015: 30 + 2 + 25 = **57%**
  [3 marks if both correct, otherwise 2 marks if one correct or 1 mark if answers are wrong but all values are read correctly from graph]
  b) C *[1 mark]*
  c) E.g. Renewable energy sources won't run out, but non-renewables will / renewable energy isn't as damaging to the environment as non-renewables *[1 mark]*.

Page 192 — Electricity and the National Grid
1 a) A *[1 mark]*
  b) potential difference: 230 V   frequency: 50 Hz *[1 mark]*
2 Current (primary coil) =
  $\frac{\text{p.d. (secondary coil)} \times \text{current (secondary coil)}}{\text{p.d. (primary coil)}}$ *[1 mark]*
  $= \frac{200\,000 \times 5}{10\,000}$ *[1 mark]*
  = **100 A** *[1 mark]*
3 The national grid uses step-up transformers to increase the potential difference of the electricity *[1 mark]*. For a given power, increasing the potential difference decreases the current *[1 mark]*. A lower current heats the wires less, so the energy lost by heating is reduced *[1 mark]*.

Page 193 — Wiring in the Home
1 a) neutral — blue
  earth — green and yellow
  live — brown
  [2 marks for all three correct, 1 mark for one correct]
  b) 0 V *[1 mark]*
  c) E.g. They would get an electric shock *[1 mark]*.
2 The plastic kettle is double insulated/made of plastic, so it can't become live if there is a fault *[1 mark]*. So there doesn't need to be an earth wire, so the earth pin doesn't need to conduct electricity *[1 mark]*.

Mixed Questions

Pages 194-198 — Biology Mixed Questions
1 a) cell membrane *[1 mark]*
  b) E.g. it has got a nucleus / it doesn't have any plasmids *[1 mark]*.
  c) D *[1 mark]*
2 a) glucose + **oxygen** → **carbon dioxide** + water
  [2 marks — 1 mark for each correct answer in bold]
  b) C *[1 mark]*
  c) From top to bottom, the steps should be numbered: 2, 4, 3, 1 *[2 marks for all four steps in the correct order, otherwise 1 mark for two steps in the correct order.]*
3 a) i) A
   ii) D
  b) i)

	R	r
R	RR	**Rr**
r	**Rr**	rr

[1 mark]

   ii) A *[1 mark]*
The genotype for wrinkled seeds is rr. From the diagram you can see that 1 out of 4 of the offspring will have the rr genotype.
4 a) i) B *[1 mark]*
   ii) polymer *[1 mark]*
  b) A *[1 mark]*
  c) i) pH 9 *[1 mark]*
   ii) The enzyme will not work *[1 mark]* because the acid will change the shape of its active site/denature the enzyme *[1 mark]* and the substrate will no longer fit *[1 mark]*.
5 a) i) photosynthesis *[1 mark]*
   ii) chloroplast *[1 mark]*
  b) C *[1 mark]*
1 mm = 1000 µm, so 45 mm will equal 45 × 1000 = 45 000 µm.
  c) i) Carbon dioxide diffuses into a leaf from the air *[1 mark]*, through the stomata *[1 mark]*.
   ii) transpiration *[1 mark]*
  d) translocation *[1 mark]*
6 a) It would have been a control. / It would have shown that it was the algae that caused any observed results *[1 mark]*.
  b) To stop light from reaching the algae cells in that tube. / To give a light intensity of 0 *[1 mark]*.
  c) Photosynthesis uses up carbon dioxide *[1 mark]*, so the algae cells in Tube 2 must have been photosynthesising because the carbon dioxide concentration decreased *[1 mark]*. The carbon dioxide concentration in Tube 1 increased *[1 mark]*, so carbon dioxide was being made and not used by the cells *[1 mark]*.
The carbon dioxide concentration in Tube 1 increased because the algae cells were respiring — aerobic respiration produces carbon dioxide.
  d) There would be no change in the amount of carbon dioxide in the tubes (so the indicator wouldn't change colour) *[1 mark]*. The enzymes in the algae cells would be destroyed by boiling, so they wouldn't be able to photosynthesise/respire *[1 mark]*.
All biological reactions (including photosynthesis and respiration) involve enzymes. Enzymes stop working at high temperatures because they are denatured, so the biological reactions will stop.

Pages 199-206 — Chemistry Mixed Questions

1 a) lithium *[1 mark]*

   b) Any one from: sodium / potassium / rubidium / caesium / francium *[1 mark]*

   c) A *[1 mark]*

   d) D *[1 mark]*

   e) i) hydrogen *[1 mark]*

   ii) E.g. add Universal indicator (or any other suitable named indicator) / use a pH meter *[1 mark]*.

2 a) C *[1 mark]*

   b) (aq) *[1 mark]*

   c) crystallisation *[1 mark]*

3 a) Sulfur impurities in fossil fuels *[1 mark]* react with oxygen from the air when the fuels are burned *[1 mark]*.

   b) E.g. acid rain *[1 mark]*.

   c) $M_r(SO_2) = 32.1 + (16.0 \times 2)$
       $= 32.1 + 32.0 = \mathbf{64.1}$ *[1 mark]*

   d) solid *[1 mark]*

4 a) mean = $(35.60 + 35.90 + 35.75) \div 3$
       $= \mathbf{35.75\ cm^3}$
       [2 marks for the correct answer, otherwise 1 mark for using the correct method.]

   b) E.g. the pH would start high/above pH 7 *[1 mark]*. As the hydrochloric acid was added the pH would decrease *[1 mark]* until it reached 7 *[1 mark]*.

   c) i) $HCl + NaOH \rightarrow NaCl + H_2O$
       [1 mark for correct reactants, 1 mark for correct products.]

   ii)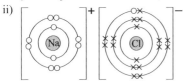
       [1 mark for adding seven crosses and one dot to outer shell of Cl⁻ ion, 1 mark for correct charge on both ions.]

   iii) ionic *[1 mark]*

5 a) hydrogen/H_2 *[1 mark]*

   b) The most reactive metal will react fastest with the acid *[1 mark]*. In reaction D the largest volume of gas has been collected in the syringe after 30 seconds / the most bubbles are being given off *[1 mark]*.

   c) zinc *[1 mark]*

   d) Gap for reaction of iron with copper sulfate: yes *[1 mark]*
       Gap for reaction of magnesium with iron sulfate: yes *[1 mark]*

6 a) 2+ *[1 mark]*

   b) chlorine *[1 mark]*.

7 a)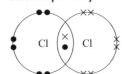
       [1 mark for shared pair of electrons, 1 mark for six further electrons in the outer shell of each chlorine atom.]

   b) Yes, the chlorine would displace iodine from sodium iodide solution *[1 mark]*, because chlorine is more reactive than iodine *[1 mark]*.

   c) B *[1 mark]*

   d) E.g. hold a piece of damp litmus paper in the gas *[1 mark]*. It will be bleached white in the presence of chlorine *[1 mark]*.

8 a) $MgCO_3 + 2HCl \rightarrow MgCl_2 + H_2O + CO_2$
       [1 mark for the formulas of all three products being correct and 1 mark for correctly balancing the equation.]

   b) It will be faster than the original reaction *[1 mark]*.

9 a) Group: 6 *[1 mark]*
       Explanation: There are 6 electrons in the outer shell *[1 mark]*.

   b) Charge: 2– *[1 mark]*
       Reason: Sulfur atoms need to gain two electrons to get a full outer shell *[1 mark]*.

10 a) Endothermic, because the temperature decreased during the reaction *[1 mark]*.

   b) The rate of reaction will increase *[1 mark]* because there will be more acid particles in the same volume *[1 mark]* so collisions between the reactant particles will be more frequent *[1 mark]*.

11 a) a piece of (filter) paper *[1 mark]*

   b) i) R_f of **A** = $4.6 \div 12.1 = \mathbf{0.38}$ *[1 mark]*

   ii) R_f of **B** = $10.6 \div 12.1 = \mathbf{0.876}$ *[1 mark]*

   c) A mixture is a substance that contains different compounds or different elements that aren't all part of a single compound *[1 mark]*.

   d) Molecular formula = $C_2H_4O_2$
       Largest number that goes into both 2 and 4 exactly = 2
       Empirical formula = CH_2O
       [2 marks for correct answer, otherwise 1 mark for writing a correct molecular formula.]

It doesn't matter if you wrote the molecular formula in a slightly different way to what we've shown here. All that matters is that you've correctly written down how many of each type of atom the molecule contains.

12 a) $2Al_2O_3 \rightarrow 4Al + 3O_2$ *[1 mark]*

   b) Any two from: e.g. recycling helps save some of the limited amount of metal ore in the earth. / Recycling cuts down on the waste sent to landfill. / Recycling is often cheaper then extracting metals from ores. / Less metal ore is mined, which means less damage to the landscape *[1 mark for each correct answer up to a maximum of 2 marks]*.

13 a) How to grade your answer:
       Level 0: There is no relevant information. *[No marks]*
       Level 1: A brief attempt is made to explain one or two of the properties in terms of structure and/or bonding. *[1 to 2 marks]*
       Level 2: Some explanation of all three properties, in terms of structure and/or bonding, is given, or a complete explanation of one or two of these properties is given. *[3 to 4 marks]*
       Level 3: A clear and detailed explanation of all three properties, in terms of both structure and bonding, is given. *[5 to 6 marks]*

Here are some points your answer may include:
Diamond
Each carbon atom in diamond forms four covalent bonds in a rigid giant covalent structure, making it very hard.
Because it is made up of lots of covalent bonds, which take a lot of energy to break, diamond has a very high melting point.
There are no free electrons in the structure of diamond, so it can't conduct electricity.
Graphite
Each carbon atom in graphite forms three covalent bonds.
The carbon atoms are arranged in layers/sheets.
There are no covalent bonds between layers, so the layers can slide over each other.
This makes graphite soft and slippery.
The covalent bonds between the carbon atoms take a lot of energy to break, giving graphite a very high melting point.
Each carbon atom has one electron which is free to move, so graphite has lots of free/electrons and can conduct electricity.

   b) 2.4 *[1 mark]*

Answers

Pages 207-212 — Physics Mixed Questions

1 a) step-up transformer *[1 mark]*
 b) E.g. coal / oil / natural gas / uranium *[1 mark]*
 c) i) E.g. they won't run out / they do less damage to the environment than non-renewables *[1 mark]*.
 ii) E.g. they are reliable / they let us respond to changes in demand / there is enough available to meet current demand *[1 mark]*.

2 a) A *[1 mark]*
 b) The vibrations in a transverse wave are at right angles to the direction that the wave is travelling in *[1 mark]*.
 c) E.g. communications / cooking *[1 mark]*.

3 a) density = mass ÷ volume
   $= 3000 ÷ 1.5 = $ **2000 kg/m³**
   [2 marks for the correct answer, otherwise 1 mark for substituting the values into the equation.]
 b) i) boiling / evaporating *[1 mark]*
 ii) E.g. the type of material stays the same / the change can be reversed easily *[1 mark]*.

4 a) B *[1 mark]*
 b) E.g. increase the current through the wire *[1 mark]*.
 c) potential difference = current × resistance
   So, resistance = potential difference ÷ current
   $= 12.0 ÷ 3.20 = $ **3.75 Ω**
   [3 marks for correct answer, otherwise 1 mark for rearranging the equation and 1 mark for substituting the numbers into the rearranged equation.]

5 a) D *[1 mark]*
 b) power = (current)² × resistance
   So, resistance = power ÷ (current)²
   $= 0.96 ÷ (0.40^2) = $ **6.0 Ω**
   [3 marks for the correct answer, otherwise 1 mark for rearranging the equation and 1 mark for substituting the values into the rearranged equation.]

6 a) Atom A and atom B *[1 mark]*. E.g. they both have the same atomic number but different mass numbers *[1 mark]*.
 b) wavelength = wave speed ÷ frequency
   $= (3.0 × 10^8) ÷ (1.5 × 10^{20})$
   $= $ **2.0 × 10⁻¹² m**
   [3 marks for correct answer, otherwise 1 mark for correct equation and 1 mark for correct substitution.]
 c) E.g. genetic mutations / cancer / tissue damage *[1 mark]*

7 a) the variable resistor / the battery *[1 mark]*
 b) i) $5.0 + 2.0 = $ **7.0 A** *[1 mark]*
 ii) current on branch with variable resistor = 5.0 A
   power = potential difference × current
   $= 9.0 × 5.0 = $ **45 W**
   [2 marks for the correct answer, otherwise 1 mark for the substituting the values into the equation.]
 c) It will have no effect on the brightness of the bulbs *[1 mark]* as the current on the branch and the voltage remain the same *[1 mark]*.

8 a) efficiency = useful output energy transfer ÷ input energy
   transfer
   So, useful output energy transfer = efficiency × input
   energy transfer
   $= 0.65 × 5000$
   $= 3250$ J
   energy wasted = $5000 − 3250 = $ **1750 J**
   [4 marks for the correct answer, otherwise 1 mark for rearranging the efficiency equation, 1 mark for substituting the values into the rearranged equation, 1 mark for subtracting the useful energy transfer from the total input energy transfer.]
 b) E.g. lubricate any moving parts *[1 mark]*.
 c) B *[1 mark]*

9 a) i) Amount of compression of the spring *[1 mark]*.
 ii) Velocity of trolley *[1 mark]*.
 b) E.g. use the same trolley each time / use the same spring each time / keep the distance between the spring and the light gate constant / keep the track horizontal each time *[1 mark]*.
 c) B *[1 mark]*
 Just multiply the speed in km/s by 1000 to find it in m/s.
 d) i) kinetic energy = 0.5 × mass × (speed)²
   $= 0.5 × 0.20 × (0.50^2) = $ **0.025 J**
   [2 marks for the correct answer, otherwise 1 mark for substituting the values into the equation.]
 ii) Average speed = distance ÷ time
   $= 0.90 ÷ 0.60$
   $= $ **1.5 m/s**
   [3 marks for correct answer, otherwise 1 mark for correctly recalling the equation and 1 mark for correct substitution.]

10 a) i)

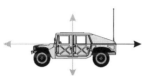

   [1 mark for an arrow in the right direction, 1 mark for it being the same length as the driving force (left-pointing) arrow.]
 ii) Force A is the car's weight,
   weight = mass × gravitational field strength
   So, mass = weight ÷ gravitational field strength
   $= 9 ÷ 10 = $ **0.9 kg**
   [3 marks for correct answer, otherwise 1 mark for correctly rearranging the equation and 1 mark for correct substitution.]
 b) The resultant force acting on the car is zero *[1 mark]*.
 c) i) work done = force × distance
   So, distance = work done ÷ force *[1 mark]*
   $= 150 ÷ 30$ *[1 mark]*
   $= $ **5 m** *[1 mark]*
 ii) The car is travelling the same distance so the same amount of energy needs to be transferred *[1 mark]*. As the car is now more powerful, the energy required will be transferred over a shorter period of time and the car will take less time to travel the distance *[1 mark]*.

CGP

www.cgpbooks.co.uk